Shepherding Winds

Shepherding Winds

An Anthology of Poetry from East and West
Chosen by James Kirkup

BLACKIE LONDON AND GLASGOW

Blackie & Son Limited,
5 Fitzhardinge Street, London, W.1
Bishopbriggs, Glasgow
Blackie & Son (India) Limited, Bombay

216.88372.5

Printed in Great Britain by Neill & Co. Ltd., Edinburgh.

'Once I lived all alone in an isolated hut near a Greek village, "shepherding winds" as a Byzantine ascetic used to say; in other words, writing poetry.'

NIKOS KAZANTZAKIS *Report to Greco*

Introduction

The character of any anthology is determined as much by what is left out as by what is put in.

In this selection I have sought to choose poems which are good in their own right and which will also be stimulating to the minds and imaginations of young people, their teachers and their parents.

I make no distinction between 'hard' and 'easy' poems. A child or a student should never be made to feel that a poem is a problem to be sweated and swotted over, but rather as a unique experience to be taken in his stride, just as he takes a new toy, a new picture, and a new song. He may not understand everything, but that does not matter: rational understanding is the least part of poetry appreciation. After all, adults too frequently encounter poems they do not entirely understand. Repeated readings – and this means reading aloud too – will make even fairly difficult poems come alive in the mind, just as constant listening to a new and strange piece of music makes it become familiar and accept-able. As long as even a small degree of contact with the poet's imagination is obtained, one can feel encouraged that young people will find their own ways to a closer understanding of the text.

Some young readers will be able to appreciate and enjoy more than others. After all, there is nothing wrong with not liking poetry or music. But the degree of enjoyment is not as important as the introduction of young minds to a whole new world of colour, sound, movement and ideas. I have tried to include as many modern poets as possible, for the modern child instinctively responds to the modern idiom in verse. It would be an exciting project to publish a poetry anthology for young people composed entirely of contemporary work and including such new elements as pop lyrics, modern folk and rock ballads, concrete poems, protest songs, and work by the very lively new provincial groups in Liverpool, on Tyneside, and in Scotland, Ireland and Wales.

In one respect this anthology is, I think, unique in that it contains many translations of Chinese and Japanese poetry, both classical and modern, by established poets and by schoolchildren. It is my experience that children and even university students – certainly American students – respond much more quickly and eagerly to the imagery, mood and forms of Oriental poetry than to those of English verse. They enjoy, too, the making (and the breaking) of mathematical rules in the counting of syllables in Japanese verse forms.

Many of the poems in this anthology are poems whose worth and suitability I have proved in teachers' training courses with my former students at Bath Academy of Arts. They have been used successfully with American children and university students, as well as with the large numbers of Japanese, Chinese, Malay, Swedish and French students I have taught.

I should like to thank all those teachers, poets and children who have made suggestions and sent poems. (Some of the children's poems were so good that I have included them in this volume.) It is impossible to name them all here, but I should like especially to mention Barry Tebb (who kindly made the selection of my own poems which he had found successful in class), Charles Causley, Rena Clayphan, Mona Pehle, Joe Ackerley, Shozo Tokunaga, Rikutaro Fukuda, Tsutomu Fukuda, Michael Bullock, Howard Sergeant, Gloria Evans Davies, Margaret Stanley-Wrench, Charles Higham, Jack Clemo, Robert Morgan, Bryn Griffiths, Haruo Shibuya and John C. Head.

Finally, I should like to express my grateful thanks to Mr and Mrs Charles Rummel of the Japan American Conversation Institute and Keio University in Tokyo for their careful typing.

JAMES KIRKUP

Amherst College
Amherst
Mass. 01002
U.S.A.

Japan Women's University
Bunkyo-ku
Tokyo
Japan

Contents

10

Countrysides

Ode on Solitude

Happy the man, whose wish and care
  A few paternal acres bound,
Content to breathe his native air,
    In his own ground.
Whose herds with milk, whose fields with bread,
  Whose flocks supply him with attire,
Whose trees in summer yield him shade,
    In winter fire.
Blest, who can unconcern'dly find
  Hours, days, and years slide soft away,
In health of body, peace of mind,
    Quiet by day,
Sound sleep by night; study and ease,
  Together mixt; sweet recreation;
And innocence, which most does please
    With meditation.
Thus let me live, unseen, unknown,
  Thus unlamented let me die,
Steal from the world, and not a stone
    Tell where I lie.

ALEXANDER POPE
1688 – 1744

A Stone

a stone
kept living
for millions of years
in silence
meanwhile
the sky
became sometimes clear
and sometimes cloudy

SHIGEJI TSUBOI
born 1889
Translated from the Japanese by
Ichiro Kono and Rikutaro Fukuda

On This Island

Look, stranger, on this island now
The leaping light for your delight discovers,
Stand stable here
And silent be,
That through the channels of the ear
May wander like a river
The swaying sound of the sea.

Here at the small field's ending pause
Where the chalk wall falls to the foam and its tall ledges
Oppose the pluck
And knock of the tide,
And the shingle scrambles after the suck-
-ing surf,
And the gull lodges
A moment on its sheer side.

Far off like floating seeds the ships
Diverge on urgent voluntary errands,
And the full view
Indeed may enter
And move in memory as now these clouds do,
That pass the harbour mirror
And all the summer through the water saunter.

W. H. AUDEN
born 1907

18

The Hurrying Brook

With half a hundred sudden loops and coils
Between the limits of two humble farms,
Swerving and dodging like a boy who foils
His mates' pursuit; with numberless wild charms;
With beauty and joy my tiny river dances
The longest way he can, and prettiest too,
About our meadows, topped with shining lances
Of reed and rush, tunnelled in shadowy blue
Of thicket oak and alder and ivied shell
Of vast old willow; fast he runs and well
To keep his many appointments all at once,
Now the eel-stone, now the yellow lily, now the white,
Now where the fat vole on the clay ledge suns,
Here there and everywhere, a brilliant watersprite.

EDMUND BLUNDEN
born 1896

Rice-Planting

From early morning the cultivator
Is roaring.
Uncle in a rubber coat walks back and forth.
Brother throws bundles of young rice plants
From the road into the flooded paddy-field.
One bundle after another
Flies like a ball, making a loud splash.
While I stand watching,
Lines of green plants are formed.
Frogs are singing loudly.

TOKIYO YAMADA
born 1952
(girl) 5th grade, Shosha School
for the Handicapped, Himeji City.
Translated from the Japanese
by Naoshi Koriyama

Amid the Barren Hills

There is a spot, 'mid barren hills,
    Where winter howls, and driving rain;
But, if the dreary tempest chills,
    There is a light that warms again.

The house is old, the trees are bare,
    Moonless above bends twilight's dome;
But what on earth is half so dear –
    So longed for – as the hearth of home?

The mute bird sitting on the stone,
    The dank moss dripping from the wall,
The thorn-trees gaunt, the walks o'ergrown,
    I love them – how I love them all! . . .

A little and a lone green lane
    That opened on a common wide;
A distant, dreamy, dim blue chain
    Of mountains, circling every side.

A heaven so clear, an earth so calm,
    So sweet, so soft, so hushed an air;
And, deepening still the dream-like charm,
    Wild moor-sheep feeding everywhere.

EMILY BRONTË
1818 – 1848

The Wayside Station

Here at the wayside station, as many a morning,
I watch the smoke torn from the fumy engine
Crawling across the field in serpent sorrow.
Flat in the east, held down by stolid clouds,
The struggling day is born and shines already
On its warm hearth far off. Yet something here
Glimmers along the ground to show the seagulls
White on the furrows' black unturning waves.

But now the light has broadened.
I watch the farmstead on the little hill,
That seems to mutter: 'Here is day again'
Unwillingly. Now the sad cattle wake
In every byre and stall,
The ploughboy stirs in the loft, the farmer groans
And feels the day like a familiar ache
Deep in his body, though the house is dark.
The lovers part
Now in the bedroom where the pillows gleam
Great and mysterious as deep hills of snow,
An inaccessible land. The wood stands waiting
While the bright snare slips coil by coil around it,
Dark silver on every branch. The lonely stream
That rode through darkness leaps the gap of light,
Its voice grown loud, and starts its winding journey
Through the day and time and war and history.

EDWIN MUIR
1887 – 1959

The Mower to the Glow-Worms

Ye living lamps, by whose dear light
The nightingale does sit so late,
And studying all the summer-night,
Her matchless songs does meditate;

Ye country comets, that portend
No war, nor princes funeral,
Shining unto no higher end
Than to presage the grass's fall;

Ye glow-worms, whose officious flame
To wand'ring mowers shows the way,
That in the night have lost their aim,
And after foolish fires do stray;

Your courteous lights in vain you waste,
Since Juliana here is come,
For she my mind hath so displac'd
That I shall never find my home.

ANDREW MARVELL
1621 – 1678

Noon on the Farm

Now the horses gently
Sway, entering golden stables.
Men like sacks lean
In holy straw-light.

In the enclosed noon,
A swollen kitten and two
Hens in brown bloomers under
Nude horses wander.

The blue-slotted whitewash and
The tiles' rococo gloom of doves
Recall the cooling summer, the tiny
Reapers in the sun.

And dead clothes abandoned under
Dark steps of corn.

JAMES KIRKUP
born 1923

The Poplar-Field

The poplars are fell'd, farewell to the shade
And the whispering sound of the cool colonnade,
The winds play no longer, and sing in the leaves,
Nor Ouse on his bosom their image receives.

Twelve years have elaps'd since I first took a view
Of my favourite field and the bank where they grew,
And now in the grass behold they are laid,
And the tree is my seat that once lent me a shade.

The blackbird has fled to another retreat
Where the hazels afford him a screen from the heat,
And the scene where his melody charm'd me before,
Resounds with his sweet-flowing ditty no more.

My fugitive years are all hasting away,
And I must ere long lie as lowly as they,
With a turf on my breast, and a stone at my head,
Ere another such grove shall arise in its stead.

'Tis a sight to engage me, if any thing can,
To muse on the perishing pleasures of man;
Though his life be a dream, his enjoyments, I see,
Have a being less durable even than he.

WILLIAM COWPER
1731 – 1800

From The Deserted Village

Sweet was the sound, when oft at evening's close,
Up yonder hill the village murmur rose;
There, as I pass'd with careless steps and slow,
The mingling notes came soften'd from below;
The swain responsive as the milk-maid sung,
The sober herd that low'd to meet their young,
The noisy geese that gabbled o'er the pool,
The playful children just let loose from school,
The watch-dog's voice that bay'd the whisp'ring wind,
And the loud laugh that spoke the vacant mind;
These all in sweet confusion sought the shade,
And fill'd each pause the nightingale had made.
But now the sounds of population fail,
No cheerful murmurs fluctuate in the gale,
No busy steps the grass-grown foot-way tread,
For all the bloomy flush of life is fled.

OLIVER GOLDSMITH
1728 – 1774

Summer Farm

Straws like tame lightnings lie about the grass
And hang zigzag on hedges. Green as glass
The water in the horse-trough shines.
Nine ducks go wobbling by in two straight lines.

A hen stares at nothing with one eye,
Then picks it up. Out of an empty sky
A swallow falls and, flickering through
The barn, dives up again into the dizzy blue.

I lie, not thinking, in the cool, soft grass,
Afraid of where a thought might take me – as
This grasshopper with plated face
Unfolds his legs and finds himself in space.

Self under self, a pile of selves I stand
Threaded on time, and with metaphysic hand
Lift the farm like a lid and see
Farm within farm, and in the centre, me.

NORMAN MACCAIG
born 1910

Inversnaid

This darksome burn, horseback brown,
His rollrock highroad roaring down,
In coop and in comb the fleece of his foam
Flutes and low to the lake falls home.

A windpuff-bonnet of fáwn-fróth
Turns and twindles over the broth
Of a pool so pitchblack, féll-frówning,
It rounds and rounds Despair to drowning.

Degged with dew, dappled with dew
Are the groins of the braes that the brook treads through,
Wiry heathpacks, flitches of fern,
And the beadbonny ash that sits over the burn.

What would the world be, once bereft
Of wet and of wildness? Let them be left,
O let them be left, wildness and wet;
Long live the weeds and the wilderness yet.

GERARD MANLEY HOPKINS
1844 – 1889

Farewell, Sweet Groves
From *Fair-Virtue*

Farewell,
Sweet groves to you;
You hills, that highest dwell,
And all you humble vales, adieu.
You wanton brooks and solitary rocks,
My dear companions all, and you, my tender flocks!
Farewell, my pipe, and all those pleasing songs, whose moving strains
Delighted once the fairest nymphs that dance upon the plains;
You discontents, whose deep and over-deadly smart,
Have, without pity, broke the truest heart;
Sighs, tears, and every sad annoy,
That erst did with me dwell,
And all other's joy,
Farewell!

Adieu,
Fair shepherdesses:
Let garlands of sad yew
Adorn your dainty golden tresses.
I, that loved you, and often with my quill
Made music that delighted fountain, grove, and hill:
I, whom you loved so, and with a sweet and chaste embrace,
(Yea, with a thousand rarer favours) would vouchsafe to grace.
I, now must leave you all alone, of love to plain;
And never pipe, nor never sing again.
I must, for evermore, be gone.
And therefore bid I you,
And every one
Adieu.

GEORGE WITHER
1588 – 1667

Sea

From **Seaweed**

When descends on the Atlantic
    The gigantic
Storm-wind of the equinox,
Landward in his wrath he scourges
    The toiling surges,
Laden with seaweed from the rocks:

From Bermuda's reefs; from edges
    Of sunken ledges,
In some far-off, bright Azore;
From Bahama, and the dashing,
    Silver-flashing
Surges of San Salvador;

From the tumbling surf, that buries
    The Orkneyan skerries,
Answering the hoarse Hebrides;
And from wrecks of ships, and drifting
    Spars, uplifting
On the desolate, rainy seas; –

Ever drifting, drifting, drifting
    On the shifting
Currents of the restless main;
Till in sheltered coves, and reaches
    Of sandy beaches,
All have found repose again.

HENRY WADSWORTH LONGFELLOW
1807 – 1882

The Stars Go over the Lonely Ocean

Unhappy about some far off things
That are not my affair, wandering
Along the coast and up the lean ridges,
I saw in the evening
The stars go over the lonely ocean,
And a black-maned wild boar
Plowing with his snout on Mal Paso Mountain.

The old monster snuffled, 'Here are sweet roots,
Fat grubs, slick beetles and sprouted acorns.
The best nation in Europe has fallen,
And that is Finland,
But the stars go over the lonely ocean,'
The old black-bristled boar,
Tearing the sod on Mal Paso Mountain.

'The world's in a bad way, my man,
And bound to be worse before it mends;
Better lie up in the mountain here
Four or five centuries,
While the stars go over the lonely ocean,'
Said the old father of wild pigs,
Plowing the fallow on Mal Paso Mountain.

'Keep clear of the dupes that talk democracy
And the dogs that bark revolution,
Drunk with talk, liars and believers,
I believe in my tusks.
Long live freedom and damn the ideologies,'
Said the gamey black-maned wild boar
Tusking the turf on Mal Paso Mountain.

ROBINSON JEFFERS
1887 – 1962

The Tide Rises, the Tide Falls

The tide rises, the tide falls,
The twilight darkens, the curlew calls;
Along the sea-sands damp and brown
The traveller hastens toward the town,
    And the tide rises, the tide falls.

Darkness settles on roofs and walls,
But the sea, the sea in the darkness calls;
The little waves, with their soft, white hands,
Efface the footprints in the sands,
    And the tide rises, the tide falls.

The morning breaks; the steeds in their stalls
Stamp and neigh, as the hostler calls;
The day returns, but nevermore
Returns the traveller to the shore,
    And the tide rises, the tide falls.

HENRY WADSWORTH LONGFELLOW
1807 – 1882

At Kisagata

At Kisagata
A cherry tree is covered
At times by the waves:
Fishermen must row their boats
Above the cherry blossoms.

MATSUO BASHŌ
1644 – 1694
Translated from the Japanese
by Donald Keene

Dover Beach

The sea is calm to-night.
The tide is full, the moon lies fair
Upon the straits; – on the French coast the light
Gleams and is gone; the cliffs of England stand,
Glimmering and vast, out in the tranquil bay.

Come to the window, sweet is the night-air!
Only, from the long line of spray
Where the sea meets the moon-blanch'd land,
Listen! you hear the grating roar
Of pebbles which the waves draw back, and fling,
At their return, up the high strand,
Begin, and cease, and then again begin,
With tremulous cadence slow, and bring
The eternal note of sadness in.

Sophocles long ago
Heard it on the Aegean, and it brought
Into his mind the turbid ebb and flow,
Of human misery; we
Find also in the sound a thought,
Hearing it by this distant northern sea.

The Sea of Faith
Was once, too, at the full, and round earth's shore
Lay like the folds of a bright girdle furl'd.
But now I only hear
Its melancholy, long, withdrawing roar,
Retreating, to the breath
Of the night-wind, down the vast edges drear
And naked shingles of the world.

Ah, love, let us be true
To one another! for the world, which seems
To lie before us like a land of dreams,
So various, so beautiful, so new,
Hath really neither joy, nor love, nor light,
Nor certitude, nor peace, nor help for pain;
And we are here as on a darkling plain
Swept with confused alarms of struggle and flight,
Where ignorant armies clash by night.

MATTHEW ARNOLD
1822 – 1888

From The Borough

Now is it pleasant in the Summer eve,
When a broad Shore retiring Waters leave,
Awhile to wait upon the firm fair Sand,
When all is calm at Sea, all still at Land;
And there the Ocean's Produce to explore,
As floating by, or rolling on the Shore;
Those living Jellies which the Flesh inflame,
Fierce as a Nettle, and from that its Name;
Some in huge masses, some that you may bring
In the small compass of a Lady's ring;
Figured by Hand divine – there's not a Gem
Wrought by Man's Art to be compar'd to them;
Soft, brilliant, tender, through the Wave they glow,
And make the Moon-beam brighter where they flow . . .

GEORGE CRABBE
1754 – 1832

The Sea Ritual

Prayer unsaid, and Mass unsung,
Deadman's dirge must still be rung:
    Dingle-dong, the dead-bells sound!
    Mermen chant his dirge around!

Wash him bloodless, smooth him fair,
Stretch his limbs, and sleek his hair:
    Dingle-dong, the dead-bells go!
    Mermen swing them to and fro!

In the wormless sand shall he
Feast for no foul gluttons be:
    Dingle-dong, the dead-bells chime!
    Mermen keep the tone and time!

We must with a tombstone brave
Shut the shark out from his grave:
    Dingle-dong, the dead-bells toll!
    Mermen dirgers ring his knoll!

Such a slab will we lay o'er him
All the dead shall rise before him!
    Dingle-dong, the dead-bells boom!
    Mermen lay him in his tomb!

GEORGE DARLEY
1795 – 1846

Sunk Lyonesse

In sea-cold Lyonesse,
When the Sabbath eve shafts down
On the roofs, walls, belfries
Of the foundered town,
The Nereids pluck their lyres
Where the green translucency beats,
And with motionless eyes at gaze
Make minstrelsy in the streets.
And the ocean water stirs
In salt-worn casemate and porch.
Plies the blunt-snouted fish
With fire in his skull for torch.
And the ringing wires resound;
And the unearthly lovely weep,
In lament of the music they make
In the sullen courts of sleep:
Whose marble flowers bloom for aye:
And – lapped by the moon-guiled tide –
Mock their carver with heart of stone,
Caged in his stone-ribbed side.

WALTER DE LA MARE
1873 – 1956

The Kraken

Below the thunders of the upper deep;
Far, far beneath in the abysmal sea,
His ancient, dreamless, uninvaded sleep
The Kraken sleepeth: faintest sunlights flee
About his shadowy sides: above him swell
Huge sponges of millennial growth and height;
And far away into the sickly light,
From many a wondrous grot and secret cell
Unnumber'd and enormous polypi
Winnow with giant arms the slumbering green.
There hath he lain for ages and will lie
Battening upon huge seaworms in his sleep,
Until the latter fire shall heat the deep;
Then once by men and angels to be seen,
In roaring he shall rise and on the surface die.

ALFRED, LORD TENNYSON
1809 – 1892

Patrolling Barnegat

Wild, wild the storm, and the sea high running,
Steady the roar of the gale, with incessant undertone muttering,
Shouts of demoniac laughter fitfully piercing and pealing,
Waves, air, midnight, their savagest trinity lashing,
Out in the shadows there milk-white combs careering,
On beachy slush and sand spirts of snow fierce slanting,
Where through the murk the easterly death-wind breasting,
Through cutting swirl and spray watchful and firm advancing,
(That in the distance! is that a wreck? is the red signal flaring?)
Slush and sand of the beach tireless till daylight wending,
Steadily, slowly, through hoarse roar never remitting,
Along the midnight edge by those milk-white combs careering,
A group of dim, weird forms, struggling, the night confronting,
That savage trinity warily watching.

WALT WHITMAN
1819 – 1892

Ship in Fog

A suffocating room
Of damp curtains
Anchors the ship.

Birds smash and flutter
Through one dark
Wall into the other.

The smothered sirens
Bark and boom.
– No drifting berg

Must enter the one
Door of this
Unleavable room.

JAMES KIRKUP
born 1923

The Estuary

The boat casts anchor.
The sailors' hearts also cast anchor.

Sea-gulls from the fresh water send a salute to a creaking rope.
Fish gather around a hole of the bilge.

The captain goes ashore with his salt-stained clothes changed;
He does not come back even when the night comes.

How many barnacles have been added to the bottom?
Each time the dusk thickens around the boat
The captain's son lights a green lamp at the prow, alone.

KAORU MARUYAMA
born 1899
Translated from the Japanese by
Ichiro Kono and Rikutaro Fukuda

From **Childe Harold's Pilgrimage**
Canto IV

There is pleasure in the pathless woods,
There is a rapture on the lonely shore,
There is society, where none intrudes,
By the deep Sea, and music in its roar:
I love not Man the less, but Nature more,
From these our interviews, in which I steal
From all I may be, or have been before,
To mingle with the Universe, and feel
What I can ne'er express, yet cannot all conceal.

Roll on, thou deep and dark blue Ocean – roll!
Ten thousand fleets sweep over thee in vain;
Man marks the earth with ruin – his control
Stops with the shore; upon the watery plain
The wrecks are all thy deed, nor doth remain
A shadow of man's ravage, save his own,
When, for a moment, like a drop of rain,
He sinks into thy depths with bubbling groan,
Without a grave, unknell'd, uncoffin'd, and unknown.

GEORGE GORDON, LORD BYRON
1788 – 1824

From **Voyages**
Stanza I

Above the fresh ruffles of the surf
Bright striped urchins flay each other with sand,
They have contrived a conquest for shell shucks,
And their fingers crumble fragments of baked weed
Gaily digging and scattering.

And in answer to their treble interjections
The sun beats lightning on the waves,
The waves fold thunder on the sand;
And could they hear me I would tell them:

O brilliant kids, frisk with your dog,
Fondle your shells and sticks, bleached
By time and the elements; but there is a line
You must not cross nor ever trust beyond it
Spry cordage of your bodies to caresses
Too lichen-faithful from too wide a breast.
The bottom of the sea is cruel.

HART CRANE
1899 – 1932

Stanzas for Music

There be none of Beauty's daughters
    With a magic like thee;
And like music on the waters
    Is thy sweet voice to me:
When, as if its sound were causing
The charmèd ocean's pausing,
The waves lie still and gleaming
And the lull'd winds seem dreaming:

And the midnight moon is weaving
    Her bright chain o'er the deep;
Whose breast is gently heaving,
    As an infant's asleep:
So the spirit bows before thee,
To listen and adore thee;
With a full but soft emotion,
Like the swell of Summer's ocean.

GEORGE GORDON, LORD BYRON
1788 – 1824

Frost, rain and snow

A Frosty Day

Grass afield wears silver thatch;
   Palings all are edged with rime;
Frost-flowers pattern round the latch;
   Cloud nor breeze dissolve the clime:

When the waves are solid floor,
   And the clods are iron-bound,
And the boughs are crystall'd hoar,
   And the red leaf nailed aground.

When the fieldfare's flight is slow,
   And a rosy vapour rim,
Now the sun is small and low,
   Belts along the region dim.

When the ice-crack flies and flaws,
   Shore to shore, with thunder shock,
Deeper than the evening daws,
   Clearer than the village clock.

When the rusty blackbird strips,
   Bunch by bunch, the coral thorn;
And the pale day-crescent dips,
   New to heaven, a slender horn.

JOHN LEICESTER WARREN, LORD DE TABLEY
1835 – 1895

Rain

I woke in the swimming dark
And heard, now sweet, now shrill,
The voice of the rain-water,
   Cold and still,

Endlessly sing; now faint,
In the distance borne away;
Now in the air float near,
   But nowhere stay;

Singing I know not what,
Echoing on and on;
Following me in sleep,
   Till night was gone.

WALTER DE LA MARE
1873 – 1956

Winter Clouds

Fluttering snow weighs down the winter clouds.
All flowers have wilted.
Up in the sky cold currents flow;
On the ground warmth still breathes.
Alone, a hero drives away tigers and leopards.
The brave have no fear of bears.
The plum tree welcomes a snowy sky,
Caring nothing for the flies frozen to death.

MAO TSE-TUNG
born 1893
Translated from the Chinese
by Jerome Ch'en and Michael Bullock

The Snow-Storm

Announced by all the trumpets of the sky,
Arrives the snow, and, driving o'er the fields,
Seems nowhere to alight: the whited air
Hides hills and woods, the river, and the heaven,
And veils the farm-house at the garden's end.
The sled and traveller stopped, the courier's feet
Delayed, all friends shut out, the housemates sit
Around the radiant fireplace, enclosed
In a tumultuous privacy of storm.

Come see the north wind's masonry.
Out of an unseen quarry evermore
Furnished with tile, the fierce artificer
Curves his white bastions with projected roof
Round every windward stake, or tree, or door.
Speeding, the myriad-handed, his wild work
So fanciful, so savage, nought cares he
For number or proportion. Mockingly,
On coop or kennel he hangs Parian wreaths;
A swan-like form invests the hidden thorn;
Fills up the farmer's lane from wall to wall,
Maugre the farmer's sighs; and at the gate
A tapering turret overtops the work.
And when his hours are numbered, and the world
Is all his own, retiring, as he were not,
Leaves, when the sun appears, astonished Art
To mimic in slow structures, stone by stone,
Built in an age, the mad wind's night-work,
The frolic architecture of the snow.

RALPH WALDO EMERSON
1803 – 1882

Lines

The cold earth slept below,
  Above the cold sky shone;
And all around, with a chilling sound,
  From caves of ice and fields of snow,
  The breath of night like death did flow
  Beneath the sinking moon.

The wintry hedge was black,
  The green grass was not seen,
The birds did rest on the bare thorn's breast,
  Whose roots, beside the pathway track,
  Had bound their folds o'er many a crack
  Which the frost had made between.

Thine eyes glowed in the glare
  Of the moon's dying light;
As a fen-fire's beam on a sluggish stream
  Gleams dimly, so the moon shone there,
  And it yellowed the strings of thy raven hair,
  That shook in the wind of night.

The moon made thy lips pale, beloved –
  The wind made thy bosom chill –
The night did shed on thy dear head
  Its frozen dew, and thou didst lie
  Where the bitter breath of the naked sky
  Might visit thee at will.

PERCY BYSSHE SHELLEY
1792 – 1822

Early Rain

After the long drought
The sun goes quickly out.
Leaf after leaf in the laden trees
Like cats' ears flick.
Dusty flowers on a dry stick
Stagger beneath the blows
Of the downpour breeze.
Each tree is a sounding drum,
And every rose
Is trampled in the hum
Of the shower's watery bees.

JAMES KIRKUP
born 1923

A Rainy Scene

Many a rainy scene I love:
The trickle in front of the window that taps on my dream in
      spring;
The spattering sound on banana leaves – that crisp ring;
The fine sprinkle that caresses my cheeks like fog;
And the cloudburst that pours down from the lightning –
I love them all, but above all, the moments just before the rain
      comes.
They are the moments, grey but pristine, translucent,
And pregnant with silent expectation,
While from the clouds, from somewhere unknown
Comes the clear call of a bird.

CHU HSIANG
1904 – 1933
Translated from the Chinese
by Kai-Yu Hsu

47

Cloud

A cloud that moves like something alive;
Now breaking apart, now getting together,
It changes its shape.
A cloud that looks like a doughnut.
A cloud that looks like a bear.
A cloud that looks like a fish's skin.
I never get tired of watching them.

HIDEYUKI TSUNO
born 1949
(boy) 7th grade, Kita School
for the Handicapped, Tokyo.
*Translated from the Japanese
by Naoshi Koriyama*

Snow in the Suburbs

Every branch big with it,
Bent every twig with it;
Every fork like a white web-foot;
Every street and pavement mute:
Some flakes have lost their way, and grope back upward, when
Meeting those meandering down they turn and ascend again.
The palings are glued together like a wall,
And there is no waft of wind with the fleecy fall.

A sparrow enters the tree,
Whereon immediately
A snow-lump thrice his own slight size
Descends on him and showers his head and eyes.
And overturns him,
And near inurns him,
And lights on a nether twig, when its brush
Starts off a volley of other lodging lumps with a rush.

The steps are a blanched slope,
Up which, with feeble hope,
A black cat comes, wide-eyed and thin;
And we take him in.

THOMAS HARDY
1840 – 1928

Snow

No breath of wind,
No gleam of sun –
Still the white snow
Whirls softly down –
Twig and bough
And blade and thorn
All in an icy
Quiet, forlorn.
Whispering, rustling,
Through the air,
On sill and stone,
Roof-everywhere,
It heaps its powdery
Crystal flakes,
Of every tree
A mountain makes;
Till pale and faint
At shut of day,
Stoops from the West
One wintry ray.
And, feathered in fire,
Where ghosts the moon,
A robin shrills
His lonely tune.

WALTER DE LA MARE
1873 – 1956

A Sheep Fair

The day arrives of the autumn fair,
  And torrents fall,
Though sheep in throngs are gathered there,
  Ten thousand all,
Sodden, with hurdles round them reared:
And, lot by lot, the pens are cleared,
And the auctioneer wrings out his beard,
And wipes his book, bedrenched and smeared,
And rakes the rain from his face with the edge of his hand,
  As torrents fall.

The wool of the ewes is like a sponge
  With the daylong rain:
Jammed tight, to turn, or lie, or lunge,
  They strive in vain.
Their horns are soft as finger-nails,
Their shepherds reek against the rails,
The tied dogs soak with tucked-in tails,
The buyers' hat-brims fill like pails,
Which spill small cascades when they shift their stand
  In the daylong rain.

Postscript
Time has trailed lengthily since met
  At Pummery Fair
Those panting thousands in their wet
  And woolly wear:
And every flock long since has bled,
And all the dripping buyers have sped,
And the hoarse auctioneer is dead,
Who 'Going – going!' so often said,
As he consigned to doom each meek, mewed band
  At Pummery Fair.

THOMAS HARDY
1840 – 1928

Seasons

Scel lem Duib

Here's a song –
stags give tongue
winter snows
summer goes.

High cold blow
sun is low
brief his day
seas give spray.

Fern clumps redden
shapes are hidden
wildgeese raise
wonted cries.

Cold now girds
wings of birds
icy time –
that's my rime.

BRIAN O'NOLAN
1911 – 1966

A Winter Fountain

A fountain
is most beautiful when the water is dried up.
Then I can draw,
in that cold space,
that which is not found there now.

I can draw
its flight shining on high
and the fall which stabs me so deeply.

YUJI KINOSHITA
born 1914
Translated from the Japanese by
Ichiro Kono and Rikutaro Fukuda

Blow, Blow, Thou Winter Wind

Blow, blow, thou winter wind,
Thou art not so unkind
As man's ingratitude;
Thy tooth is not so keen
Because thou art not seen,
Although thy breath be rude.
Heigh ho! sing, heigh ho! unto the green holly:
Most friendship is feigning, most loving mere folly:
Then heigh ho, the holly!
This life is most jolly.

Freeze, freeze, thou bitter sky,
That dost not bite so nigh
As benefits forgot:
Though thou the waters warp,
Thy sting is not so sharp
As friend remember'd not.
Heigh ho! sing, heigh ho! unto the green holly:
Most friendship is feigning, most loving mere folly:
Then heigh ho, the holly!
This life is most jolly.

WILLIAM SHAKESPEARE
1564 – 1616

A Certain Slant of Light

There's a certain slant of light,
On winter afternoons,
That oppresses, like the weight
Of cathedral tunes.

Heavenly hurt it gives us;
We can find no scar,
But internal difference
Where the meanings are.

None may teach it anything,
'Tis the seal, despair, –
An imperial affliction
Sent us of the air.

When it comes, the landscape listens,
Shadows hold their breath;
When it goes, 'tis like the distance
On the look of death.

EMILY DICKINSON
1830 – 1886

No!

No sun – no moon!
No morn – no noon –
No dawn – no dusk – no proper time of day –
No sky – no earthly view –
No distance looking blue –
No road – no street – no 't'other side the way' –
No end to any Row –
No indications where the Crescents go –
No top to any steeple –
No recognitions of familiar people –
No courtesies for showing 'em –
No knowing 'em! –
No travelling at all – no locomotion,
No inkling of the way – no notion –
'No go' – by land or ocean –
No mail – no post –
No news from any foreign coast –
No Park – no Ring – no afternoon gentility –
No company – no nobility –
No warmth, no cheerfulness, no healthful ease,
No comfortable feel in any member –
No shade, no shine, no butterflies, no bees,
No fruits, no flowers, no leaves, no birds, –
November!

THOMAS HOOD
1799 – 1845

Easter

I got me flowers to straw Thy way,
  I got me boughs off many a tree;
But Thou wast up by break of day,
  And brought'st Thy sweets along with Thee.

Yet though my flowers be lost, they say
  A heart can never come too late;
Teach it to sing Thy praise this day,
  And then this day my life shall date.

GEORGE HERBERT
1593 – 1633

Spring Pools

These pools that, though in forests, still reflect
The total sky almost without defect,
And like the flowers beside them, chill and shiver,
Will like the flowers beside them soon be gone,
And yet not out by any brook or river,
But up by roots to bring dark foliage on.

The trees that have it in their pent-up buds
To darken nature and be summer woods –
Let them think twice before they use their powers
To blot out and drink up and sweep away
These flowery waters and these watery flowers
From snow that melted only yesterday.

ROBERT FROST
1875 – 1964

The Question

I dreamed that, as I wandered by the way,
  Bare Winter suddenly was changed to Spring,
And gentle odours led my steps astray,
  Mixed with a sound of waters murmuring
Along a shelving bank of turf, which lay
  Under a copse, and hardly dared to fling
Its green arms round the bosom of the stream,
But kissed it and then fled, as thou mightest in dream.

There grew pied wind-flowers and violets,
  Daisies, those pearled Arcturi of the earth,
The constellated flower that never sets;
  Faint oxslips; tender bluebells, at whose birth
The sod scarce heaved; and that tall flower that wets –
  Like a child, half in tenderness and mirth –
Its mother's face with Heaven's collected tears,
When the low wind, its playmate's voice, it hears.

And in the warm hedge grew lush eglantine,
  Green cowbind and the moonlight-coloured may,
And cherry-blossoms, and white cups, whose wine
  Was the bright dew, yet drained not by the day;
And wild roses, and ivy serpentine,
  With its dark buds and leaves, wandering astray;
And flowers azure, black, and streaked with gold,
Fairer than any wakened eyes behold.

And nearer to the river's trembling edge
  There grew broad flag-flowers, purple pranked with white,
And starry river buds among the sedge,
  And floating water-lilies, broad and bright,
Which lit the oak that overhung the hedge
  With moonlight beams of their own watery light;
And bulrushes, and reeds of such deep green
As soothed the dazzled eye with sober sheen.

Methought that of these visionary flowers
  I made a nosegay, bound in such a way
That the same hues, which in their natural bowers
  Were mingled or opposed, the like array
Kept these imprisoned children of the Hours
  Within my hand, – and then, elate and gay,
I hastened to the spot whence I had come,
That I might there present it! – Oh! to whom?

PERCY BYSSHE SHELLEY
1792 – 1822

spring is like a perhaps hand

Spring is like a perhaps hand
(which comes carefully
out of Nowhere) arranging
a window, into which people look (while
people stare
arranging and changing placing
carefully there a strange
thing and a known thing here) and

changing everything carefully

spring is like a perhaps
Hand in a window
(carefully to
and fro moving New and
Old things, while
people stare carefully
moving a perhaps
fraction of flower here placing
an inch of air there) and

without breaking anything.

E. E. CUMMINGS
1894 – 1962

The Spirit of Spring

A little open-top boat
Floats on warm spring water:
A man, barefoot and in a short jacket
Stands astern, rowing an oar.
A woman wearing ordinary clothes but no powder or rouge,
Paddles in the middle of the boat;
In her arm is a child, dressed in red and green.

The cadence of their oars, one in front and one behind,
  Their merry chatter
  And unrestrained laughter,
And the child looking left and right,
  Listening with his eyes wide open,
  And gurgling . . .
A little open-top boat
Sails along to the cadence of the oars, of the chatter and
    laughter, and of the songs.
The boat
Is loaded with love
And life,
Which overflow the boat.
Their love
And their life
Also fill the sky and the water:
The spirit of spring thus better captured than by the blossoms
    and willows.

LIU TA-PAI
1880 – 1932
*Translated from the Chinese
by Kai-Yu Hsu*

60

The Green Spring

When spring comes
I see the woods turning green,
The water in the river turning green,
The hills turning green,
The fields turning green,
The little beetles turning green,
And even the white-bearded old man turning green.
The green blood
Nurtures the fatigued earth,
And from the earth bursts forth
A green hope.

SHAN MEI
*Translated from the Chinese
by Kai-Yu Hsu*

From **The Spring**

Now that the winter's gone, the earth hath lost
Her snow-white robes, and now no more the frost
Candies the grasse, or castes an ycie creame
Upon the silver Lake, or Chrystall streame:
But the warme Sunne thawes the benummed Earth,
And makes it tender, gives a sacred birth
To the dead Swallow; wakes in hollow tree
The drowzie Cuckow, and the Humble-Bee.
Now doe a quire of chirping Minstrels bring
In tryumph to the world, the youthfull Spring.
The Vallies, hills, and woods, in rich araye,
Welcome the comming of the long'd for May.

THOMAS CAREW
1595? – 1639?

Summer

Winter is cold-hearted,
  Spring is yea and nay,
Autumn is a weather-cock
  Blown every way:
Summer days for me
When every leaf is on its tree;

When Robin's not a beggar,
  And Jenny Wren's a bride,
And larks hang singing, singing, singing,
  Over the wheat-fields wide,
  And anchored lilies ride,
And the pendulum spider
  Swings from side to side,

And blue-black beetles transact business,
  And gnats fly in a host,
And furry caterpillars hasten
  That no time be lost,
And moths grow fat and thrive,
And ladybirds arrive.

Before green apples blush,
  Before green nuts embrown,
Why, one day in the country
  Is worth a month in town;
  Is worth a day and a year
Of the dusty, musty, lag-last fashion
  That days drone elsewhere.

CHRISTINA ROSSETTI
1830 – 1894

An August Midnight

A shaded lamp and a waving blind,
And the beat of a clock from a distant floor:
On this scene enter – winged, horned, and spined –
A longlegs, a moth, and a dumbledore;
While 'mid my page there idly stands
A sleepy fly, that rubs its hands . . .

Thus meet we five, in this still place,
At this point of time, at this point in space.
– My guests besmear my new-penned line,
Or bang at the lamp, and fall supine.
'God's humblest, they!' I muse. Yet why?
They know Earth-secrets that know not I.

THOMAS HARDY
1840 – 1928

Thunder and Lightning

Blood punches through every vein
As lightning strips the windowpane.

Under its flashing whip, a white
Village leaps to light.

On tubs of thunder, fists of rain
Slog it out of sight again.

Blood punches the heart with fright
As rain belts the village night.

JAMES KIRKUP
born 1923

Summer Evening

The frog, half fearful, jumps across the path,
And little mouse that leaves its hole at eve
Nimbles with timid dread beneath the swath;
My rustling steps awhile their joys deceive,
Till past – and then the cricket sings more strong,
And grasshoppers in merry moods still wear
The short night weary with their fretting song.
Up from behind the mole-hill jumps the hare,
Cheat of his chosen bed, and from the bank
The yellowhammer flutters in short fears
From off its nest hid in the grasses rank,
And drops again when no more noise it hears.
Thus nature's human link and endless thrall,
Proud man, still seems the enemy of all.

JOHN CLARE
1793 – 1864

Autumn

A touch of cold in the Autumn night –
I walked abroad,
And saw the ruddy moon lean over a hedge
Like a red-faced farmer.
I did not stop to speak, but nodded,
And round about were the wistful stars
With white faces like town children.

THOMAS ERNEST HULME
1883 – 1917

Gold Fan

Autumn is departing –
shaken by the invisible sleeves of big gingko leaves,
the rains of fans flitter and sprinkle;
I take in my hand each gold fan
that has dropped in endless dances,
and find on each fan the same word,
yes, on each and every fan.

SHIZUE UEDA
born 1898
Translated from the Japanese
by Shozo Tokunaga

Mist

Low-anchored cloud,
Newfoundland air,
Fountain-head and source of rivers,
Dew-cloth, dream drapery,
And napkin spread by fays;
Drifting meadow of the air,
Where bloom the daisied banks and violets,
And in whose fenny labyrinth
The bittern booms and heron wades;
Spirit of lakes and seas and rivers,
Bear only perfumes and the scent
Of healing herbs to just men's fields!

HENRY DAVID THOREAU
1817 – 1862

The Scent of Autumn

Who has smelled the scent of autumn
While looking at a garden from a window with tattered
    curtains?
From distant lakes
The scent of rotten leaves fallen on the marshes,
And from the depth of a forest
The smell of ripe berries on withered branches
Are brought here by a cool breeze –
The scent of autumn?
The scent
Wakes me up from an old dream,
So faint
Like the autumn clouds this moment
Being blown along by the western wind,
And again blown away,
As I gaze at them from the window.

LI KUANG-T'IEN
born 1907
Translated from the Chinese
by Kai-Yu Hsu

Autumn Loneliness

Loneliness does not
Originate in any one
Particular thing:
Evening in autumn over
The black pines of the mountain.

THE PRIEST JAKUREN
died 1202
Translated from the Japanese
by Donald Keene

Field of Autumn

Slow moves the acid breath of noon
over the copper-coated hill,
slow from the wild crab's bearded breast
the palsied apples fall.

Like coloured smoke the day hangs fire,
taking the village without sound;
the vulture-headed sun lies low
chained to the violet ground.

The horse upon the rocky height
rolls all the valley in his eye,
but dares not raise his foot or move
his shoulder from the fly.

The sheep, snail-backed against the wall,
lifts her blind face but does not know
the cry her blackened tongue gives forth
is the first bleat of snow.

Each bird and stone, each roof and well,
feels the gold foot of autumn pass;
each spider binds with glittering snare
the splintered bones of grass.

Slow moves the hour that sucks our life,
slow drops the late wasp from the pear,
the rose tree's thread of scent draws thin –
and snaps upon the air.

LAURIE LEE
born 1914

The Burning of the Leaves

Now is the time for the burning of the leaves.
They go to the fire; the nostril pricks with smoke
Wandering slowly into a weeping mist.
Brittle and blotched, ragged and rotten sheaves!
A flame seizes the smouldering ruin, and bites
On stubborn stalks that crackle as they resist.

The last hollyhock's fallen tower is dust:
All the spices of June are a bitter reek,
All the extravagant riches spent and mean.
All burns! The reddest rose is a ghost;
Sparks whirl up, to expire in the mist: the wild
Fingers of fire are making corruption clean.

Now is the time for stripping the spirit bare,
Time for the burning of days ended and done,
Idle solace of things that have gone before:
Rootless hope and fruitless desire are there;
Let them go to the fire, with never a look behind.
The world that was ours is a world that is ours no more.

They will come again, the leaf and the flower, to arise
From squalor of rottenness into the old splendour,
And magical scents to a wondering memory bring;
The same glory, to shine upon different eyes.
Earth cares for her own ruins, naught for ours.
Nothing is certain, only the certain spring.

LAURENCE BINYON
1869 – 1943

Fruit and flowers

Apples

Behold the apples' rounded worlds:
juice-green of July rain,
the black polestar of flower, the rind
mapped with its crimson stain.

The russet, crab and cottage red
burn to the sun's hot brass,
then drop like sweat from every branch
and bubble in the grass.

They lie as wanton as they fall,
and where they fall and break,
the stallion clamps his crunching jaws,
the starling stabs his beak.

In each plump gourd the cidery bite
of boys' teeth tears the skin;
the waltzing wasp consumes his share,
the bent worm enters in.

I, with as easy hunger, take
entire my season's dole;
welcome the ripe, the sweet, the sour,
the hollow and the whole.

LAURIE LEE
born 1914

The Hydrangea

The Hydrangea
That bloomed in the rain
Droops her head,
Saying, 'The rainwater is heavy'.

YASUE SAKAE
born 1953
(girl) 4th grade, Shosha School
for the Handicapped, Himeji City
Translated from the Japanese
by Naoshi Koriyama

To Blossoms

Fair pledges of a fruitful tree,
    Why do ye fall so fast?
    Your date is not so past
But you may stay yet here awhile
    To blush and gently smile,
        And go at last.

What! were ye born to be
    An hour or half's delight,
    And so to bid good night?
'Twas pity Nature brought ye forth
    Merely to show your worth
        And lose you quite.

But you are lovely leaves, where we
    May read how soon things have
    Their end, though ne'er so brave:
And after they have shown their pride
    Like you awhile, they glide
        Into the grave.

ROBERT HERRICK
1591 – 1674

The Woodspurge

The wind flapped loose, the wind was still,
Shaken out dead from tree and hill:
I had walked on at the wind's will, –
I sat now, for the wind was still.

Between my knees my forehead was, –
My lips, drawn in, said not Alas!
My hair was over in the grass,
My naked ears heard the day pass.

My eyes, wide open, had the run
Of some ten weeds to fix upon;
Among those few, out of the sun,
The woodspurge flowered, three cups in one.

From perfect grief there need not be
Wisdom or even memory:
One thing then learnt remains to me, –
The woodspurge has a cup of three.

DANTE GABRIEL ROSSETTI
1828 – 1882

Study of Two Pears

Opusculum paedagogum.
The pears are not viols,
Nudes or bottles.
They resemble nothing else.

They are yellow forms
Composed of curves
Bulging toward the base.
They are touched red.

They are not flat surfaces
Having curved outlines.
They are round
Tapering toward the top.

In the way they are modelled
There are bits of blue.
A hard dry leaf hangs
From the stem.

The yellow glistens.
It glistens with various yellows,
Citrons, oranges and greens
Flowering over the skin.

The shadows of the pears
Are blobs on the green cloth.
The pears are not seen
As the observer wills.

WALLACE STEVENS
1879 – 1955

Nantucket

Flowers through the window
lavender and yellow

changed by white curtains –
Smell of cleanliness –

Sunshine of late afternoon –
On the glass tray

a glass pitcher, the tumbler
turned down, by which

a key is lying – And the
immaculate white bed

WILLIAM CARLOS WILLIAMS
1883 – 1963

Anemone

When I paint you
I mix ultramarine with vermilion.
O tell me, Anemone,
How can you paint your petals so
When there is no ultramarine or vermilion
Or even red or yellow
In the ground?

KAZUMASA NAKAGAWA
born 1893
Translated from the Japanese by
Ichiro Kono and Rikutaro Fukuda

To Daffodils

Fair daffodils, we weep to see
　You haste away so soon:
As yet the early-rising sun
　Has not attain'd his noon.
　　Stay, stay,
　Until the hasting day
　　Has run
　But to the even-song;
And, having pray'd together, we
　Will go with you along.

We have short time to stay, as you,
　We have as short a spring;
As quick a growth to meet decay,
　As you, or any thing.
　　We die,
　As your hours do, and dry
　　Away,
　Like to the summer's rain;
Or as the pearls of morning's dew,
　Ne'er to be found again.

ROBERT HERRICK
1591 – 1674

Fellow creatures

The Tyger

Tyger! Tyger! burning bright
In the forests of the night,
What immortal hand or eye
Could frame thy fearful symmetry?

In what distant deeps or skies
Burnt the fire of thine eyes?
On what wings dare he aspire?
What the hand dare seize the fire?

And what shoulder, and what art,
Could twist the sinews of thy heart?
And when thy heart began to beat,
What dread hand? and what dread feet?

What the hammer? what the chain?
In what furnace was thy brain?
What the anvil? what dread grasp
Dare its deadly terrors clasp?

When the stars threw down their spears
And water'd heaven with their tears,
Did he smile his work to see?
Did he who made the Lamb make thee?

Tyger! Tyger! burning bright
In the forests of the night,
What immortal hand or eye,
Dare frame thy fearful symmetry?

WILLIAM BLAKE
1757 – 1827

From **Auguries of Innocence**

To see a World in a Grain of Sand,
And a Heaven in a Wild Flower,
Hold Infinity in the palm of your hand,
And Eternity in an hour.

A Robin Red breast in a Cage
Puts all Heaven in a Rage.
A dove house fill'd with doves and Pigeons
Shudders Hell thro' all its regions.
A dog starv'd at his Master's Gate
Predicts the ruin of the State.
A Horse misus'd upon the Road
Calls to Heaven for Human blood.
Each outcry of the hunted Hare
A fibre from the Brain does tear.
A Skylark wounded in the wing,
A Cherubim does cease to sing.
The Game Cock clipt and arm'd for fight
Does the Rising Sun affright.
Every Wolf's and Lion's howl
Raises from Hell a Human Soul.
The wild deer, wand'ring here and there
Keeps the Human Soul from Care.
The Lamb misus'd breeds Public strife,
And yet forgives the Butcher's Knife.
The Bat that flits at close of Eve
Has left the Brain that won't Believe.
The Owl that calls upon the Night
Speaks the Unbeliever's fright.
He who shall hurt the little Wren
Shall never be belov'd by Men.
He who the Ox to wrath has mov'd
Shall never be by Woman lov'd.
The wanton Boy that kills the Fly
Shall feel the Spider's enmity.

He who torments the Chafer's sprite
Weaves a bower in endless Night.
The Catterpiller on the Leaf
Repeats to thee thy Mother's grief.
Kill not the Moth nor Butterfly,
For the Last Judgement draweth nigh.

WILLIAM BLAKE
1757 – 1827

The Sloth

In moving-slow he has no Peer.
You ask him something in his ear;
He thinks about it for a Year;

And then, before he says a Word
There, upside down (unlike a Bird)
He will assume that you have Heard –

A most Ex-as-per-at-ing Lug.
But should you call his manner Smug,
He'll sigh and give his Branch a Hug;

Then off again to Sleep he goes,
Still swaying gently by his Toes,
And you just know he knows he knows.

THEODORE ROETHKE
1908 – 1963

Considering the Snail

The snail pushes through a green
night, for the grass is heavy
with water and meets over
the bright path he makes, where rain
has darkened the earth's dark. He
moves in a wood of desire,

pale antlers barely stirring
as he hunts. I cannot tell
what power is at work, drenched there
with purpose, knowing nothing.
What is a snail's fury? All
I think is that if later

I parted the blades above
the tunnel and saw the thin
trail of broken white across
litter, I would never have
imagined the slow passion
to that deliberate progress.

THOM GUNN
born 1929

The Fox

The fox is an animal
Red and thin
Walking in the mist of the blue night.
The flowers do bloom in the early mist.
When the fox goes down his earth as quick as quick
He's red as a rose.

PHILIP WONNACOTT
born 1957

The Snare

I hear a sudden cry of pain!
   There is a rabbit in a snare:
Now I hear the cry again,
   But I cannot tell from where.

But I cannot tell from where
   He is calling out for aid;
Crying on the frightened air,
   Making everything afraid,

Making everything afraid,
   Wrinkling up his little face,
As he cries again for aid;
   – And I cannot find the place!

And I cannot find the place
   Where his paw is in the snare;
Little one! Oh, little one!
   I am searching everywhere.

JAMES STEPHENS
1882 – 1950

Mouse's Nest

I found a ball of grass among the hay
And progged it as I passed and went away;
And when I looked I fancied something stirred,
And turned agen and hoped to catch the bird –
When out an old mouse bolted in the wheats
With all her young ones hanging at her teats;
She looked so odd and so grotesque to me,
I ran and wondered what the thing could be,
And pushed the knapweed bunches where I stood;
Then the mouse hurried from the craking brood.
The young ones squeaked, and as I went away
She found her nest again among the hay.
The water o'er the pebbles scarce could run
And broad old cesspools glittered in the sun.

JOHN CLARE
1793 – 1864

Cat

The cat, though innocent tonight, allows
Its eyes, that sometimes drowse,
Sometimes to move in anguish. Idle cat,
Too self-contented to remember that
Sometimes the lights go out; too fat to care;
Too certain that the certain dark will wear
Of all rare stars yours starriest, most rare.

YAMAMURA BOCHŌ
1884 – 1924
Translated from the Japanese
by Graeme Wilson

84

Man and Beast

Hugging the ground by the lilac tree,
With shadows in conspiracy,

The black cat from the house next door
Waits with death in each bared claw

For the tender unwary bird
That all the summer I have heard

In the orchard singing. I hate
The cat that is its savage fate,

And choose a stone with which to send
Slayer, not victim, to its end.

I look to where the black cat lies,
But drop my stone, seeing its eyes –

Who is it sins now, those eyes say,
You the hunter, or I the prey?

CLIFFORD DYMENT
born 1914

Epitaph on a Hare

Here lies, whom hound did ne'er pursue,
    Nor swifter greyhound follow,
Whose foot ne'er tainted morning dew,
    Nor ear heard huntsman's hallo',

Old Tiney, surliest of his kind,
    Who, nurs'd with tender care,
And to domestic bounds confin'd,
    Was still a wild Jack-hare.

Though duly from my hand he took
    His pittance ev'ry night,
He did it with a jealous look,
    And, when he could, would bite.

His diet was of wheaten bread,
    And milk, and oats, and straw,
Thistles, or lettuces instead,
    With sand to scour his maw.

On twigs of hawthorn he regal'd,
    On pippins' russet peel;
And, when his juicy salads fail'd,
    Slic'd carrot pleas'd him well.

A Turkey carpet was his lawn,
    Whereon he lov'd to bound,
To skip and gambol like a fawn,
    And swing his rump around.

His frisking was at evening hours,
    For then he lost his fear;
But most before approaching show'rs,
    Or when a storm drew near.

Eight years and five round-rolling moons
   He thus saw steal away,
Dozing out all his idle noons,
   And ev'ry night at play.

I kept him for his humour's sake,
   For he would oft beguile
My heart of thoughts that made it ache,
   And force me to a smile.

But now beneath his walnut shade
   He finds his long, last home,
And waits in snug concealment laid,
   Till gentler Puss shall come.

He, still more agèd, feels the shocks
   From which no care can save,
And, partner once of Tiney's box,
   Must soon partake his grave.

WILLIAM COWPER
1731 – 1800

The Lamb

Little Lamb, who made thee?
Dost thou know who made thee?
Gave thee life and bid thee feed
By the stream and o'er the mead;
Gave thee clothing of delight,
Softest clothing, woolly, bright;
Gave thee such a tender voice,
Making all the vales rejoice?
Little Lamb, who made thee?
Dost thou know who made thee?

Little Lamb, I'll tell thee,
Little Lamb, I'll tell thee:
He is callèd by thy name,
For he calls himself a Lamb,
He is meek, and he is mild;
He became a little child.
I a child and thou a lamb,
We are callèd by his name.
Little Lamb, God bless thee!
Little Lamb, God bless thee!

WILLIAM BLAKE
1757 – 1827

The Thought-Fox

I imagine this midnight moment's forest:
Something else is alive
Beside the clock's loneliness
And this blank page where my fingers move.

Through the window I see no star:
Something more near
Though deeper within darkness
Is entering the loneliness:

Cold, delicately as the dark snow,
A fox's nose touches twig, leaf;
Two eyes serve a movement, that now
And again now, and now, and now

Sets neat prints into the snow
Between trees, and warily a lame
Shadow lags by stump and in hollow
Of a body that is bold to come

Across clearings, an eye,
A widening deepening greenness,
Brilliantly, concentratedly,
Doming about its own business

Till, with a sudden sharp hot stink of fox
It enters the dark hole of the head.
The window is starless still; the clock ticks,
The page is printed.

TED HUGHES
born 1930

The Sheep

Slowly they pass
In the grey of the evening
Over the wet road,
A flock of sheep.
Slowly they wend
In the grey of the gloaming
Over the wet road
That winds through the town.
Slowly they pass,
And gleaming whitely
Vanish away
In the grey of the evening.
Ah, what memories
Loom for a moment,
Gleam for a moment,
And vanish away,
Of the white days
When we two together
Went in the evening
Where the sheep lay,
We two together,
Went with slow feet
In the grey of the evening,
Where the sheep lay.
Whitely they gleam
For a moment, and vanish
Away in the dimness
Of sorrowful years,
Gleam for a moment,
All white, and go fading
Away in the greyness
Of sundering years.

SEUMAS O'SULLIVAN
1879 – 1958

A Rat

Having cast away
This life of death-in-life,
A rat lay in a heap in the middle of the road,
Like a bas-relief.

Before long the rat became flat.
All kinds of wheels
Came gliding along
And like an iron flattened the rat.

The rat became thinner and thinner –
The thinner and thinner he became
The rat
Ceased to be the '*rat*' of 'a rat'
Or the '*a*' rat,
And even the shadow of death disappeared.

One day when I came out into the road for a look,
A sheet of something flat was lying there,
Beaten and warped by the sun.

BAKU YAMANOGUCHI
1903 – 1963
Translated from the Japanese
by Shozo Tokunaga

The Horses

I climbed through woods in the hour-before-dawn dark.
Evil air, a frost-making stillness,

Not a leaf, not a bird, –
A world cast in frost. I came out above the wood

Where my breath left tortuous statues in the iron light.
But the valleys were draining the darkness

Till the moorline – blackening dregs of the brightening grey –
Halved the sky ahead. And I saw the horses:

Huge in the dense grey – ten together –
Megalith-still. They breathed, making no move,

With draped manes and tilted hind-hooves,
Making no sound.

I passed: not one snorted or jerked its head.
Grey silent fragments

Of a grey silent world.

I listened in emptiness on the moor-ridge.
The curlew's tear turned its edge on the silence.

Slowly detail leafed from the darkness. Then the sun
Orange, red, red erupted

Silently, and splitting to its core tore and flung cloud,
Shook the gulf open, showed blue,

And the big planets hanging –.
I turned

Stumbling in the fever of a dream, down towards
The dark woods, from the kindling tops,

And came to the horses. There, still they stood,
But now steaming and glistening under the flow of light,

Their draped stone manes, their tilted hind-hooves
Stirring under a thaw while all around them

The frost showed its fires. But still they made no sound.
Not one snorted or stamped,

Their hung heads patient as the horizons,
High over valleys, in the red levelling rays –

In din of the crowded streets, going among the years, the faces,
May I still meet my memory in so lonely a place

Between the streams and the red clouds, hearing curlews,
Hearing the horizons endure.

TED HUGHES
born 1930

On a Favourite Cat, Drowned in a Tub of Gold Fishes

'Twas on a lofty vase's side,
Where China's gayest art had dyed
   The azure flowers that blow;
Demurest of the tabby kind,
The pensive Selima reclined,
   Gazed on the lake below.

Her conscious tail her joy declared;
The fair round face, the snowy beard,
   The velvet of her paws,
Her coat, that with the tortoise vies,
Her ears of jet, and emerald eyes,
   She saw; and purr'd applause.

Still had she gazed; but 'midst the tide
Two angel forms were seen to glide,
   The Genii of the stream:
Their scaly armour's Tyrian hue
Thro' richest purple to the view
   Betray'd a golden gleam.

The hapless Nymph with wonder saw:
A whisker first, and then a claw,
   With many an ardent wish,
She stretch'd in vain to reach the prize.
What female heart can gold despise?
   What Cat's averse to fish?

Presumptuous Maid! with looks intent
Again she stretch'd, again she bent,
   Nor knew the gulf between.
(Malignant Fate sat by, and smiled.)
The slipp'ry verge her feet beguiled,
   She tumbled headlong in.

Eight times emerging from the flood
She mew'd to ev'ry wat'ry god,
  Some speedy aid to send.
No Dolphin came, no Nereid stirr'd:
Nor cruel *Tom*, nor *Susan* heard.
  A Fav'rite has no friend!

From hence, ye Beauties, undeceived,
Know, one false step is ne'er retrieved,
  And be with caution bold.
Not all that tempts your wand'ring eyes
And heedless hearts, is lawful prize;
  Nor all that glisters, gold.

THOMAS GRAY
1716 – 1771

Engraved on the Collar of a Dog
which I Gave to His Royal Highness

I am his Highness' dog at Kew;
Pray tell me, sir, whose dog are you?

ALEXANDER POPE
1688 – 1744

The Bat

Lightless, unholy, eldritch thing,
Whose murky and erratic wing
Swoops so sickenly, and whose
Aspect to the female Muse
Is a demon's, made of stuff
Like tattered, sooty waterproof,
Looking dirty, clammy, cold.

Wicked, poisonous, and old;
I have maligned thee! . . . for the Cat
Lately caught a little bat,
Seized it softly, bore it in.
On the carpet, dark as sin
In the lamplight, painfully
It limped about, and could not fly.

Even fear must yield to love,
And pity makes the depths to move.
Though sick with horror, I must stoop,
Grasp it gently, take it up,
And carry it, and place it where
It could resume the twilight air.

Strange revelation! warm as milk,
Clean as a flower, smooth as silk!
O what a piteous face appears,
What great fine thin translucent ears!
What chestnut down and crapy wings,
Finer than any lady's things –
And O a little one that clings!

Warm, clean, and lovely, though not fair,
And burdened with a mother's care;
Go hunt the hurtful fly, and bear
My blessing to your kind in air.

RUTH PITTER
born 1897

My Cats
(a Witch speaks)

I like to toss him up and down
A heavy cat weighs half a Crown
With a hey do diddle my cat Brown.

I like to pinch him on the sly
When nobody is passing by
With a hey do diddle my cat Fry.

I like to ruffle up his pride
And watch him skip and turn aside
With a hey do diddle my cat Hyde.

Hey Brown and Fry and Hyde my cats
That sit on tombstones for your mats.

STEVIE SMITH
born Hull

A Dog in Snow

Overnight the world has become delft china,
White, with dark blue shadows of snow. The trees
Brush plumes across the down of clouds, the smaller
Feathers drift as snow. And over the whiteness
My red dog runs, printing his sudden black
Cloves from trefoil paws. An ember in the snow
He darts from bush to bush like a wavering flame,
And in his joy sets fire to the cold ground.

MARGARET STANLEY-WRENCH
born 1916

The National Health Cow

I strolled into a farmyard
When no one was about
Treading past the troubles
I raised my head to shout.

'Come out the Cow with glasses,'
I called and rolled my eye.
It ambled up toward me,
I milked it with a sigh.

'You're just in time' the cow said,
Its eyes were all aglaze,
'I'm feeling like an elephant,
I aren't been milked for days.'

'Why is this?' I asked it,
Tugging at its throttles.
'I don't know why, perhaps it's 'cause
My milk comes out in bottles.'

'That's handy for the government,'
I thought, and in a tick
The cow fell dead all sudden
(I'd smashed it with a brick).

JOHN LENNON
born 1940

Camel

In your pupils
There must be reflected a vast sea of desert,
The blood-red setting sun rolling down at the farthest end of the
    desert,
And green oases
Under the leaves of palm-trees descried on the horizon.
Gentleness of your pupils
Makes me feel your distant dreams.
But, what is this fence here?
What is this patch of sand here?
And you are eating the bread a child has thrown
With a peaceful look on your face.
Is your nostalgia already buried
Deep in your body?
Or is it because these people gathered here
Have taken from you the dreams of your great motherland
Of Sphinx and pyramids?

KOICHI KIHARA
born 1922
Translated from the Japanese
by Ichiro Kono and Rikutaro Fukuda

99

Kangaroo

In the northern hemisphere
Life seems to leap at the air, or skim under the wind
Like stags on rocky ground, or pawing horses, or springy
    scut-tailed rabbits.

Or else rush horizontal to charge at the sky's horizon,
Like bulls or bisons or wild pigs.

Or slip like water slippery towards its ends,
As foxes, stoats, and wolves, and prairie dogs.

Only mice, and moles, and rats, and badgers, and beavers, and
    perhaps bears
Seem belly-plumbed to the earth's mid-navel.
Or frogs that when they leap come flop, and flop to the centre
    of the earth.

But the yellow antipodal Kangaroo, when she sits up,
Who can unseat her, like a liquid drop that is heavy, and just
    touches earth.

The downward drip.
The down-urge.
So much denser than cold-blooded frogs.

Delicate mother Kangaroo
Sitting up there rabbit-wise, but huge, plumb-weighted,
And lifting her beautiful slender face, oh! so much more gently
    and finely lined than a rabbit's, or than a hare's,
Lifting her face to nibble at a round white peppermint drop
    which she loves, sensitive mother Kangaroo.

Her sensitive, long, pure-bred face.
Her full antipodal eyes, so dark,
So big and quiet and remote, having watched so many empty
    dawns in silent Australia.

Her little loose hands, and drooping Victorian shoulders.
And then her great weight below the waist, her vast pale belly
With a thin young yellow little paw hanging out, and straggle
    of a long thin ear, like ribbon,
Like a funny trimming to the middle of her belly, thin little
    dangle of an immature paw, and one thin ear.

Her belly, her big haunches
And, in addition, the great muscular python-stretch of her tail.

There, she shan't have any more peppermint drops.
So she wistfully, sensitively sniffs the air, and then turns, goes
    off in slow sad leaps

On the long flat skis of her legs,
Steered and propelled by that steel-strong snake of a tail.

Stops again, half turns, inquisitive to look back.
While something stirs quickly in her belly, and a lean little face
    comes out, as from a window,
Peaked and a bit dismayed,
Only to disappear again quickly away from the sight of the
    world, to snuggle down in the warmth,
Leaving the trail of a different paw hanging out.

Still she watches with eternal, cocked wistfulness!
How full her eyes are, like the full, fathomless, shining eyes of
    an Australian black-boy
Who has been lost so many centuries on the margins of
    existence!

She watches with insatiable wistfulness.
Untold centuries of watching for something to come,
For a new signal from life, in that silent lost land of the South.

Where nothing bites but insects and snakes and the sun, small
    life.
Where no bull roared, no cow ever lowed, no stag cried, no
    leopard screeched, no lion coughed, no dog barked,
But all was silent save for parrots occasionally, in the haunted
    blue bush.

Wistfully watching, with wonderful liquid eyes.
And all her weight, all her blood, dripping sack-wise down
    towards the earth's centre,
And the live little one taking in its paw at the door of her belly.

Leap then, and come down on the line that draws to the earth's
    deep, heavy centre.

D. H. LAWRENCE
1885 – 1930

From Song of Myself

I think I could turn and live with animals, they are so placid
    and self-contained;
I stand and look at them long and long.
They do not sweat and whine about their condition;
They do not lie awake in the dark and weep for their sins;
They do not make me sick discussing their duty to God;
Not one is dissatisfied – not one is demented with the mania of
    owning things;
Not one kneels to another, nor to his kind that lived thousands
    of years ago;
Not one is respectable or industrious over the whole earth.

WALT WHITMAN
1819 – 1892

Birds

A Bird Came down the Walk

A bird came down the walk:
He did not know I saw;
He bit an angle-worm in halves
And ate the fellow, raw.

And then he drank a dew
From a convenient grass,
And then hopped sidewise to the wall
To let a beetle pass.

He glanced with rapid eyes
That hurried all abroad, –
They looked like frightened beads, I thought
He stirred his velvet head

Like one in danger; cautious,
I offered him a crumb,
And he unrolled his feathers
And rowed him softer home

Than oars divide the ocean,
Too silver for a seam,
Or butterflies, off banks of noon,
Leap, plashless, as they swim.

EMILY DICKINSON
1830 – 1886

The Eagle

He clasps the crag with crooked hands;
Close to the sun in lonely lands,
Ring'd with the azure world, he stands.

The wrinkled sea beneath him crawls;
He watches from his mountain walls,
And like a thunderbolt he falls.

ALFRED, LORD TENNYSON
1809 – 1892

The Birds
From *Milton* Book II

Thou hearest the Nightingale begin the Song of Spring:
The Lark, sitting upon his earthy bed, just as the morn
Appears, listens silent; then, springing from the waving corn-
    field, loud
He leads the Choir of Day – trill! trill! trill! trill!
Mounting upon the wings of light into the Great Expanse,
Re-echoing against the lovely blue and shining heavenly Shell;
His little throat labours with inspiration; every feather
On throat and breast and wings vibrates with the effluence
    Divine.
All Nature listens silent to him, and the awful Sun
Stands still upon the mountain looking on this little Bird
With eyes of soft humility and wonder, love and awe.
Then loud from their green covert all the Birds begin their song:
The Thrush, the Linnet and the Goldfinch, Robin and the Wren
Awake the Sun from his sweet revery upon the mountain:
The Nightingale again assays his song, and thro' the day
And thro' the night warbles luxuriant; every Bird of song
Attending his loud harmony with admiration and love.

WILLIAM BLAKE
1757 – 1827

The Twa Corbies

As I was walking all alane,
I heard twa corbies making a mane:
The tane unto the tither did say,
'Whar sall we gang and dine the day?'

'– In behint yon auld fail dyke
I wot there lies a new-slain knight;
And naebody kens that he lies there
But his hawk, his hound, and his lady fair.

'His hound is to the hunting gane,
His hawk to fetch the wild-fowl hame,
His lady's ta'en another mate,
So we may mak' our dinner sweet.

'Ye'll sit on his white hause-bane,
And I'll pike out his bonny blue e'en:
Wi' ae lock o' his gowden hair
We'll theek our nest when it grows bare.

'Mony a one for him maks mane,
But nane sall ken whar he is gane:
O'er his white banes, when they are bare,
The wind sall blaw for evermair.'

ANON.

corbies, ravens   *fail*, turf   *hause-bane*, neck-bone   *theek*, thatch

From **The Lark Ascending**

He rises and begins to round,
He drops the silver chain of sound,
Of many links without a break,
In chirrup, whistle, slur and shake,
All intervolved and spreading wide,
Like water-dimples down a tide
Where ripple ripple overcurls
And eddy into eddy whirls;
A press of hurried notes that run
So fleet they scarce are more than one,
Yet changeingly the trills repeat
And linger ringing while they fleet,
Sweet to the quick o' the ear, and dear
To her beyond the handmaid ear,
Who sits beside our inner springs,
Too often dry for this he brings,
Which seems the very jet of earth
At sight of sun, her music's mirth,
As up he winds the spiral stair,
A song of light, and pierces air
With fountain ardour, fountain play,
To reach the shining tops of day,
And drink in everything discerned
An ecstasy to music turned,
Impelled by what his happy bill
Disperses; drinking, showering still,
Unthinking save that he may give
His voice the outlet, there to live
Renewed in endless notes of glee,
So thirsty of his voice is he,
For all to hear and all to know
That he is joy, awake, aglow,
The tumult of the heart to hear
Through pureness filtered crystal-clear,
And know the pleasure sprinkled bright
By simple singing of delight,
Shrill, irreflective, unrestrained,
Rapt, ringing, on the jet sustained.

GEORGE MEREDITH
1828 – 1909

The Wild Swans at Coole

The trees are in their autumn beauty,
The woodland paths are dry,
Under the October twilight the water
Mirrors a still sky;
Upon the brimming water among the stones
Are nine-and-fifty swans.

The nineteenth autumn has come upon me
Since I first made my count;
I saw, before I had well finished,
All suddenly mount
And scatter wheeling in great broken rings
Upon their clamorous wings.

I have looked upon those brilliant creatures,
And now my heart is sore.
All's changed since I, hearing at twilight,
The first time on this shore,
The bell-beat of their wings above my head,
Trod with a lighter tread.

Unwearied still, lover by lover,
They paddle in the cold
Companionable streams or climb the air;
Their hearts have not grown old;
Passion or conquest, wander where they will,
Attend upon them still.

But now they drift on the still water,
Mysterious, beautiful;
Among what rushes will they build,
By what lake's edge or pool
Delight men's eyes when I awake some day
To find they have flown away?

WILLIAM BUTLER YEATS
1865 – 1939

At Porthcothan

A speck of dark at low tide on the tideline,
It could not be identified as any known thing
Until, as one approached, a neck was clear
(And it is agreed that logs, or cans, are neckless),
And then a body, over which the neck stood
Curved like a question-mark, emerged
As oval, and the whole shape was crouching
Helpless in a small pool the sea had left.

The oval body, with green sheen as of pollen
Shading off into the black plumage, and the neck
Surmounted by the tiny wide-eyed head,
Were not without beauty. The head was moving,
So like a cobra it seemed rash to offer
An introductory finger to the long hooked bill
That stabbed at air. Danger had so
Sharpened what intelligence the bird possessed,
It seemed to pierce the mind of the observer.
In fact we were afraid, yes afraid of each other.

Finally though I picked it up and took it
To a quiet side-bay where dogs were rarer.
Here the shag sat, happy in the sun,
Perched on a slab of rock where a pool was
In which I caught five fish for it
With a pocketknife, a handkerchief
And a plunging forefinger. But at six o'clock
It left the rock and waddled off seaward.

Though breakers came in high and curling
It straddled them, bouncing, buoyant,
Borne along the sealine sideways, with head up,
Slithering across the bay's whole width, and then
Drifted ashore again, to scuttle flapping
With webbed feet flat like a Saturday banker's
To shelter on a level rock. Here it studied,
With the air of one of whom something is expected,
The turbulent Atlantic slowly rising.
What could I do but leave it meditating?

Early next morning on the bay's north side
I found it cuddled under the cliff; the tide
Was low again. What hungry darkness
Had driven so the dark young shag to shelter?
It did not resist when I picked it up.
Something had squeezed the cobra out of it.

I took it to a cave where the sun shone in,
Then caught two fish. It opened one green eye,
And then another. But though I cut
The fish into portions, presenting these
To the bill's hooked tip, it only shook its head.
Noon came. The shag slept in the cave. At two
I hurried back. The shag was stone dead,
With its fine glossy head laid back a little
Over the left shoulder, and a few flies
Were pestering its throat and the fish scraps
Now unlikely to get eaten.

          Ten minutes perhaps
I sat there, then carried it up the cliff path
And across the headland to a neighbouring cove
Where oystercatchers and hawks flew and far
Far below in loose heaps small timber lay, tickled
By a thin finger of sea. There I flung the shag,
For in some such place, I thought,
Such bodies best belong, far from bathers, among
The elements that compose and decompose them,
Unconscious, strange to freedom, but perceptible
Through narrow slits that score the skin of things.
Or perhaps (for I could not see the body falling)
A hand rose out of air and plucked the corpse
From its arc and took it, warm still,
To some safer place and concealed it there,
Quite unobtrusively, but sure, but sure.

CHRISTOPHER MIDDLETON
born 1926

The Jackdaw

There is a bird who, by his coat,
And by the hoarseness of his note,
    Might be suppos'd a crow;
A great frequenter of the church,
Where, bishop-like, he finds a perch,
    And dormitory too.

Above the steeple shines a plate,
That turns and turns, to indicate
    From what point blows the weather.
Look up – your brains begin to swim,
'Tis in the clouds – that pleases him,
    He chooses it the rather.

Fond of the speculative height,
Thither he wings his airy flight,
    And thence securely sees
The bustle and the raree-show
That occupy mankind below,
    Secure and at his ease.

You think, no doubt, he sits and muses
On future broken bones and bruises,
    If he should chance to fall.
No; not a single thought like that
Employs his philosophic pate,
    Or troubles it at all.

He sees that this great roundabout –
The world, with all its motley rout,
    Church, army, physic, law,
Its customs, and its businesses, –
Is no concern at all of his,
    And says – what says he? – Caw.

Thrice happy bird! I too have seen
Much of the vanities of men;
    And, sick of having seen 'em,
Would cheerfully these limbs resign
For such a pair of wings as thine,
    And such a head between 'em.

WILLIAM COWPER
1731 – 1800

The Dalliance of the Eagles

Skirting the river road, (my forenoon walk, my rest,)
Skyward in air a sudden muffled sound, the dalliance of the
    eagles,
The rushing amorous contact high in space together,
The clinching interlocking claws, a living, fierce, gyrating wheel,
Four beating wings, two beaks, a swirling mass tight grappling,
In tumbling turning clustering loops, straight downward falling,
Till o'er the river pois'd, the twain yet one, a moment's lull,
A motionless still balance in the air, then parting, talons
    loosing,
Upward again on slow-firm pinions slanting, their separate
    diverse flight,
She hers, he his, pursuing.

WALT WHITMAN
1819 – 1892

In My Garden

To-day, within my garden arch,
    From the woodbine clustering round,
A dainty little wren down flew,
    And tripped along the ground.

Nearer the pretty stranger came,
    With pert and saucy pride,
Then nimbly hopped upon the seat,
    And waited by my side.

Quiet I sat like one transfixed –
    The sight was strange and new –
And wondered in my inmost heart
    What next the wren would do.

Awhile it stood, so pert and trim –
    My breath came soft and slow –
Now held its little head aside,
    And bobbed it to and fro;

Then, in a second, up it flew,
    Its little wings outspread,
Beneath the woodbine in the roof
    And perched upon my head.

I could have cried aloud with joy
    To feel its tiny weight,
But like a statue I remained,
    And still upon the seat.

Then off the little stranger went,
    And straight away it flew,
And out towards the elm-tree tops,
    Like a speck against the blue.

And now I know, what long I felt,
    With pain so sweet and wild,
That Nature holds me in her thought,
    And claims me for her child.

ALFRED WILLIAMS
1832 – 1905

Cock-Crow

Out of the wood of thoughts that grows by night
To be cut down by the sharp axe of light, –
Out of the night, two cocks together crow,
Cleaving the darkness with a silver blow:
And bright before my eyes twin trumpeters stand,
Heralds of splendour, one at either hand,
Each facing each as in a coat of arms:
The milkers lace their boots up at the farms.

EDWARD THOMAS
1878 – 1917

Cuckoos

When coltsfoot withers and begins to wear
Long silver locks instead of golden hair,
And fat red catkins from black poplars fall
And on the ground like caterpillars crawl,
And bracken lifts up slender arms and wrists
And stretches them, unfolding sleepy fists,
The cuckoos in a few well-chosen words
Tell they give Easter eggs to the small birds.

ANDREW YOUNG
born 1885

Fish and others

From **The Fish, the Man, and the Spirit**

To a Fish

You strange, astonished-looking, angle-faced,
   Dreary-mouthed, gaping wretches of the sea,
   Gulping salt water everlastingly,
Cold-blooded, though with red your blood be graced,
And mute, though dwellers in the roaring waste;
   And you, all shapes beside, that fishy be, –
   Some round, some flat, some long, all devilry,
Legless, unloving, infamously chaste: –

O scaly, slippery, wet, swift, staring wights,
   What is't ye do? What life lead? Eh, dull goggles?
How do ye vary your vile days and nights?
   How pass your Sundays? Are ye still but joggles
In ceaseless wash? Still nought but gapes, and bites,
   And drinks, and stares, diversified with boggles?

A Fish Answers

Amazing monster! that, for aught I know,
   With the first sight of thee didst make our race
   For ever stare! O flat and shocking face,
Grimly divided from the breast below!
Thou that on dry land horribly dost go
   With a split body and most ridiculous pace,
   Prong after prong, disgracer of all grace,
Long-useless-finned, haired, upright, unwet, slow!

O breather of unbreathable, sword-sharp air,
   How canst exist? How bear thyself, thou dry
And dreary sloth? What particle canst share
   Of the only blessed life, the watery?
I sometimes see of ye an actual *pair*
   Go by! linked fin by fin! most odiously.

LEIGH HUNT
1784 – 1859

119

The Fish

I caught a tremendous fish
and held him beside the boat
half out of water, with my hook
fast in a corner of his mouth.
He didn't fight.
He hadn't fought at all.
He hung a grunting weight,
battered and venerable
and homely. Here and there
his brown skin hung in strips
like ancient wall-paper,
and its pattern of darker brown
was like wall-paper:
shapes like full-blown roses
stained and lost through age.
He was speckled with barnacles,
fine rosettes of lime,
and infested
with tiny white sea-lice,
and underneath two or three
rags of green weed hung down.
While his gills were breathing in
the terrible oxygen
– the frightening gills
fresh and crisp with blood,
that can cut so badly –
I thought of the coarse white flesh
packed in like feathers,
the big bones and the little bones,
the dramatic reds and blacks
of his shiny entrails,
and the pink swim-bladder
like a big peony.
I looked into his eyes
which were far larger than mine
but shallower, and yellowed,
the irises backed and packed
with tarnished tinfoil
seen through the lenses
of old scratched isinglass.

They shifted a little, but not
to return my stare.
– It was more like the tipping
of an object toward the light.
I admired his sullen face,
the mechanism of his jaw,
and then I saw
that from his lower lip
– if you could call it a lip –
grim, wet and weapon-like,
hung five old pieces of fish-line,
or four and a wire leader
with the swivel still attached,
with all their five big hooks
grown firmly in his mouth.
A green line, frayed at the end
where he broke it, two heavier lines,
and a fine black thread
still crimped from the strain and snap
when it broke and he got away.
Like medals with their ribbons
frayed and wavering,
a five-haired beard of wisdom
trailing from his aching jaw.
I stared and stared
and victory filled up
the little rented boat,
from the pool of bilge
where oil had spread a rainbow
around the rusted engine
to the bailer rusted orange,
the sun-cracked thwarts,
the oarlocks on their strings,
the gunnels – until everything
was rainbow, rainbow, rainbow!
And I let the fish go.

ELIZABETH BISHOP
born 1911

An Octopus which Did Not Die

A starving octopus was kept in a water-tank of an aquarium for a long time. The light through the pale glass ceiling drifted sadly behind the dark shadow of a rock in the tank.

Everbody had forgotten about this dark water-tank. The octopus was supposed to have been dead for quite a while, and only the rotten sea-water was seen left in the glass tank dimly lighted by the dusty sunshine.

But the creature was not dead; the octopus was hidden behind the rock. And when he awoke from his sleep he had to suffer from cruel starvation for days and days in this merciless, deserted tank. There was no bait, no food left for him to eat; he started eating his legs. One, at first. Then, another. When all of his legs were gone, he turned his inside out, and started eating a part of his insides, bit by bit, from one part to another.

Thus, the octopus finished eating all his body; his skin, his brain, his stomach – everything, all over, completely.

One morning a watchman came by and looked into the tank only to find the indigo-coloured water and the swaying sea-weeds in the dirty glass tank. There was no living creature in any corner of the rock. The octopus had actually disappeared.

But, the octopus was not dead. Long after he was gone, still he was there, eternally alive in that musty, empty, deserted water-tank of the aquarium. For centuries – perhaps eternally – an invisible creature with a dire scarcity and dissatisfaction was there, alive.

SAKUTARO HAGIWARA
1886 – 1942
Translated from the Japanese
by Ichiro Kono and Rikutaro Fukuda

The Maldive Shark

About the Shark, phlegmatical one,
Pale sot of the Maldive sea,
The sleek little pilot-fish, azure and slim,
How alert in attendance be.
From his saw-pit of mouth, from his charnel of maw
They have nothing of harm to dread,
But liquidly glide on his ghastly flank
Or before his Gorgonian head;
Or lurk in the port of serrated teeth
In white triple tiers of glittering gates,
And there find a haven when peril's abroad,
An asylum in jaws of the Fates!
They are friends; and friendly they guide him to prey,
Yet never partake of the treat –
Eyes and brains to the dotard lethargic and dull,
Pale ravener of horrible meat.

HERMAN MELVILLE
1819 – 1891

A Crocodile

Hard by the lilied Nile I saw
A duskish river-dragon stretched along,
The brown habergeon of his limbs enamelled
With sanguine alamandines and rainy pearl:
And on his back there lay a young one sleeping,
No bigger than a mouse; with eyes like beads,
And a small fragment of its speckled egg
Remaining on its harmless, pulpy snout;
A thing to laugh at, as it gaped to catch
The baulking merry flies. In the iron jaws
Of the great devil-beast, like a pale soul
Fluttering in rocky hell, lightsomely flew
A snowy trochilus, with roseate beak
Tearing the hairy leeches from his throat.

THOMAS LOVELL BEDDOES
1803 – 1849

The Pike

From shadows of rich oaks outpeer
The moss-green bastions of the weir,
Where the quick dipper forages
In elver-peopled crevices,
And a small runlet trickling down the sluice
Gossamer music tires not to unloose.

Else round the broad pool's hush
    Nothing stirs,
Unless sometimes a straggling heifer crush
Through the thronged spinney where the pheasant whirs;
    Or martins in a flash
Come with wild mirth to dip their magical wings;
While in the shallow some doomed bulrush swings
At whose hid root the diver vole's teeth gnash.

124

And nigh this toppling reed, still as the dead
  The great pike lies, the murderous patriarch
  Watching the waterpit sheer-shelving dark,
Where through the plash his lithe bright vassals thread.

    The rose-finned roach and bluish bream
    And staring ruffe steal up the stream
    Hard by their glutted tyrant, now
    Still as a sunken bough.

    He on the sandbank lies,
      Sunning himself long hours
    With stony gorgon eyes:
      Westward the hot sun lowers.

Sudden the gray pike changes, and quivering poises for
        slaughter;
    Intense terror wakens around him, the shoals scud
        awry, but there chances
    A chub unsuspecting; the prowling fins quicken, in
        fury he lances;
And the miller that opens the hatch stands amazed at the
        whirl in the water.

                    EDMUND BLUNDEN
                    born 1896

Song of the Mackerel Pike

O! Autumn winds,
If you have any pity at all,
Go and tell her for his sake –
That a man is sitting here
Alone at his supper table
Eating broiled pike,
And lost in thoughts of his wife gone away.

Mackerel pike,
Over which the man
(After the fashion of his folk at home)
Squeezes the sour juice of a green tangerine
And eats the fish –
Curious, then endearing
This rustic habit in the man –
She used always to bring for his supper
Such a freshly-picked green tangerine . . .

A pitiful sight –
The wife who is to be forsaken by her husband
And the husband betrayed by his wife
Sit facing each other across the supper table;
While a little girl, unloved by her father,
Is struggling, sadness in her heart,
With her own tiny chopsticks,
Trying to offer this man who is not her father
A bit of her own fish.

O! Autumn winds,
Behold this homely gathering,
A sight out of this world –
Autumn winds,
Prove that this
Happy gathering is not just a dream.

O! Autumn winds,
If you have any heart,
Go and say to
The wife whose husband has not yet deserted her
And the little girl whose father has not yet gone away
That a man is sitting here
Alone at his supper table
Eating broiled pike,
And letting fall salty tears.

O! Mackerel pike,
Are you salt or bitter?
In what land is it the custom
To eat mackerel pike
With hot tears squeezed over it?
O! Is the question I am asking quite absurd?

HARUO SATŌ
born 1892
Translated from the Japanese
by Shozo Tokunaga

The Best of Fishes in my Flood

The best of fishes in my flood
Shall give themselves to be her food.
The trout, the dace, the pike, the bream,
The eel, that loves the troubled stream,
The miller's thumb, the hiding loach,
The perch, the ever-nibbling roach,
The shoats with whom is Tavy fraught,
The foolish gudgeon, quickly caught,
And last the little minnow-fish,
Whose chief delight in gravel is.
 In right she cannot me despise
Because so low mine empire lies.
For I could tell how Nature's store
Of majesty appeareth more
In waters than in all the rest
Of elements.

WILLIAM BROWNE, of Tavistock
1591 – 1643

Insects

I

Flying Crooked

The butterfly, a cabbage-white,
(His honest idiocy of flight)
Will never now, it is too late,
Master the art of flying straight,
Yet has – who knows so well as I ? –
A just sense of how not to fly :
He lurches here and here by guess
And God and hope and hopelessness.
Even the aerobatic swift
Has not his flying-crooked gift.

ROBERT GRAVES
born 1895

A Butterfly

Even on this cloudy day, a butterfly is flying.
A white butterfly,
High and low.
Isn't this an amazing thing?
Where was she
Resting her wings,
Trembling,
When it was raining cats and dogs?

SHINKICHI TAKAHASHI
born 1901
Translated from the Japanese
by Ichiro Kono and Rikutaro Fukuda

The Study of a Spider

From holy flower to holy flower
Thou weavest thine unhallowed bower.
The harmless dewdrops, beaded thin,
Ripple along thy ropes of sin.
Thy house a grave, a gulf thy throne
Affright the fairies every one.
Thy winding sheets are grey and fell,
Imprisoning with nets of hell
The lovely births that winnow by,
Winged sisters of the rainbow sky:
Elf-darlings, fluffy, bee-bright things,
And owl-white moths with mealy wings,
And tiny flies, as gauzy thin
As e'er were shut electrum in.
These are thy death spoils, insect ghoul,
With their dear life thy fangs are foul.
Thou felon anchorite of pain
Who sittest in a world of slain.
Hermit, who tunest song unsweet
To heaving wing and writhing feet.
A glutton of creation's sighs,
Miser of many miseries.

Toper, whose lonely feasting chair
Sways in inhospitable air.
The board is bare, the bloated host
Drinks to himself toast after toast.
His lip requires no goblet brink,
But like a weasel must he drink.
The vintage is as old as time
And bright as sunset, pressed and prime.

Ah venom mouth and shaggy thighs
And paunch grown sleek with sacrifice,
Thy dolphin back and shoulders round
Coarse-hairy as some goblin hound
Whom a hag rides to sabbath on,
While shuddering stars in fear grow wan.
Thou palace priest of treachery,
Thou type of selfish lechery,
I break the toils around thy head
And from their gibbets take thy dead.

JOHN LEICESTER WARREN, LORD DE TABLEY
1835 – 1895

White Butterfly

What wisdom do you offer me,
Little white butterfly?
You open your wordless pages, and
Close again your wordless pages.

In your opened pages:
Solitude;
In your closed pages:
Solitude.

TAI WANG-SHU
1905 – 1950
*Translated from the Chinese
by Kai-Yu Hsu*

The Fly

Little Fly,
Thy summer's play
My thoughtless hand
Has brush'd away.

Am not I
A fly like thee?
Or art not thou
A man like me?

For I dance,
And drink, and sing,
Till some blind hand
Shall brush my wing.

If thought is life
And strength and breath,
And the want
Of thought is death;

Then am I
A happy fly,
If I live
Or if I die.

WILLIAM BLAKE
1757 – 1827

The Bee

Like trains of cars on tracks of plush
I hear the level bee:
A jar across the flowers goes,
Their velvet masonry

Withstands until the sweet assault
Their chivalry consumes,
While he, victorious, tilts away
To vanquish other blooms.

His feet are shod with gauze,
His helmet is of gold;
His breast, a single onyx
With chrysoprase, inlaid.

His labor is a chant,
His idleness a tune;
Oh, for a bee's experience
Of clovers and of noon!

EMILY DICKINSON
1830 – 1886

The Gnat

One Night all tired with the weary Day,
And with my tedious selfe, I went to lay
      My fruitlesse Cares
      And needlesse feares
         Asleep.
The Curtaines of the Bed, and of mine Eyes
Being drawne, I hop'd no trouble would surprise
      That Rest which now
      'Gan on my Brow
         To creep.

When loe a little flie, lesse than its Name
(It was a Gnat) with angry Murmur came.
      About She flew,
      And lowder grew
         Whilst I
Fain would have scorn'd the silly Thing, and slept
Out all its Noise; I resolute silence kept,
      And laboured so
      To overthrow
         The Flie.

But still with sharp Alarms vexatious She
Or challenged, or rather mocked Me.
      Angry at last
      About I cast
         My Hand.
'Twas well Night would not let me blush, nor see
With whom I fought; And yet though feeble She
      Nor Her nor my
      Owne Wrath could I
         Command.

Away She flies, and Her owne Triumph sings;
I being left to fight with idler Things,
        A feeble pair
        My selfe and Aire.
           How true
A worme is Man, whom flies their sport can make!
Poor worme; true Rest in no Bed can he take,
        But one of Earth,
        Whence He came forth
           And grew.

For there None but his silent Sisters be,
Wormes of as true and genuine Earth as He,
        Which from the same
        Corruption came:
           And there
Though on his Eyes they feed, though on his Heart
They neither vex nor wake Him; every part
        Rests in sound sleep,
        And out doth keep
           All feare.

JOSEPH BEAUMONT
1616 – 1699

The Fly

How large unto the tiny fly
  Must little things appear! –
A rosebud like a feather bed,
  Its prickle like a spear;

A dewdrop like a looking-glass,
  A hair like golden wire;
The smallest grain of mustard-seed
  As fierce as coals of fire;

A loaf of bread, a lofty hill;
  A wasp, a cruel leopard;
And specks of salt as bright to see
  As lambkins to a shepherd.

WALTER DE LA MARE
1873 – 1956

House and home

The House on the Hill

They are all gone away,
  The House is shut and still,
There is nothing more to say.

Through broken walls and gray
  The winds blow bleak and shrill:
They are all gone away.

Nor is there one today
  To speak them good or ill:
There is nothing more to say.

Why is it then we stray
  Around that sunken sill?
They are all gone away.

And our poor fancy-play
  For them is wasted skill:
There is nothing more to say.

There is ruin and decay
  In the House on the Hill:
They are all gone away,
There is nothing more to say.

EDWIN ARLINGTON ROBINSON
1869 – 1935

I Know Some Lonely Houses off the Road

I know some lonely houses off the road
A robber'd like the look of, –
Wooden barred,
And windows hanging low,
Inviting to
A portico,

Where two could creep:
One hand the tools,
The other peep
To make sure all's asleep.
Old-fashioned eyes,
Not easy to surprise!

How orderly the kitchen'd look by night,
With just a clock, –
But they could gag the tick,
And mice won't bark;
And so the walls don't tell,
None will.

A pair of spectacles ajar just stir –
An almanac's aware.
Was it the mat winked,
Or a nervous star?
The moon slides down the stair
To see who's there.

There's plunder, – where?
Tankard, or spoon,
Earring, or stone,
A watch, some ancient brooch
To match the grandmamma,
Staid sleeping there.

Day rattles, too,
Stealth's slow;
The sun has got as far
As the third sycamore.
Screams chanticleer,
'Who's there?'

And echoes, trains away,
Sneer – 'Where?'
While the old couple, just astir,
Think that the sunrise left the door ajar!

EMILY DICKINSON
1830 – 1886

Washing Day

The chalk-lined tub, like a coral basin, is choked with
    soap and water.
Clusters of still bubbles, from the bottom rise,
Exploding into steam blown eyes.
Soapy, shimmering bubbles rise, dilate and burst.
Foggy patches in the kitchen linger,
Clinging to the window with a running finger.
Steam drifts up, pricking mum's plagued cheeks,
Her coarse red hands glissade into water,
Her sore face portraying gnawing anger.
Outside, her warm wet hands and face are horse-whipped
    by the wind,
The billowing washing, pouches and prances,
In ghostly uniformity chaotically dances.

D. H. THOMAS
born 1948

The Little Cart

The little cart jolting and banging through the yellow haze of
    dusk.
  The man pushing behind: the woman pulling in front.
They have left the city and do not know where to go.
'Green, green, those elm-tree leaves: *they* will cure my
    hunger,
If only we could find some quiet place and sup on them
    together.'

The wind has flattened the yellow mother-wort:
Above it in the distance they see the walls of a house.
  '*There* surely must be people living who'll give you something
    to eat.'
  They tap at the door, but no one comes: they look in, but
    the kitchen is empty.
  They stand hesitating in the lonely road and their tears fall
    like rain.

CH'EN TZU-LUNG
*Translated from the Chinese
by Arthur Waley*

The Wind Tapped Like a Tired Man

The wind tapped like a tired man,
And like a host, 'Come in,'
I boldly answered: entered then
My residence within

A rapid, footless guest,
To offer whom a chair
Were as impossible as hand
A sofa to the air.

No bone had he to bind him,
His speech was like the push
Of numerous humming-birds at once
From a superior bush.

His countenance a billow,
His fingers, as he passed,
Let go a music, as of tunes
Blown tremulous in glass.

He visited, still flitting,
Then, like a timid man,
Again he tapped – 'twas flurriedly –
And I became alone.

EMILY DICKINSON
1830 – 1886

Moonlit Apples

At the top of the house the apples are laid in rows,
And the skylight lets the moonlight in, and those
Apples are deep-sea apples of green. There goes
    A cloud on the moon in the autumn night.

A mouse in the wainscot scratches, and scratches, and then
There is no sound at the top of the house of men
Or mice; and the cloud is blown and the moon again
    Dapples the apples with deep-sea light.

They are lying in rows there, under the gloomy beams,
On the sagging floor; they gather the silver streams
Out of the moon, those moonlit apples of dreams,
    And quiet is the steep stair under.

In the corridors under there is nothing but sleep.
And stiller than ever on orchard boughs they keep
Tryst with the moon, and deep is the silence, deep
    On moon-washed apples of wonder.

JOHN DRINKWATER
1882 – 1937

146

The Country Bedroom

My room's a square and candle-lighted boat,
In the surrounding depths of night afloat.
My windows are the portholes, and the seas
The sound of rain on the dark apple-trees.

Sea monster-like beneath, an old horse blows
A snort of darkness from his sleeping nose,
Below, among drowned daisies. Far off, hark!
Far off one owl amidst the waves of dark.

FRANCES CORNFORD
1886 – 1960

My Dog

After supper
I gave the cat his meal,
And I also gave the dog his meal.
When we all the family were watching television,
The dog raised a bark.
Suddenly I thought he must be asking for water.
Then I brought him some.
And he drank it up quickly.
When he looked up at me,
As if he were asking for more,
His eyes glistened in the dark.
I flew back to the kitchen.

KAZUHIKO NAKANISHI
born 1952
(boy) 7th grade, Shosha School
for the Handicapped, Himeji City.
*Translated from the Japanese
by Naoshi Koriyama*

Verses on Blenheim
(After Lucius Valerius Martialis)

See, here's the grand approach,
That way is for his grace's coach;
There lies the bridge, and there the clock,
Observe the lion and the cock;
The spacious court, the colonnade,
And mind how wide the hall is made;
The chimneys are so well designed,
They never smoke in any wind:
The galleries contrived for walking,
The windows to retire and talk in;
The council-chamber to debate,
And all the rest are rooms of state.
Thanks, sir, cried I, 'tis very fine,
But where d'ye sleep, or where d'ye dine?
I find by all you have been telling
That 'tis a house, but not a dwelling.

JONATHAN SWIFT
1667 – 1743

Night and day

When I Heard the Learn'd Astronomer

When I heard the learn'd astronomer,
When the proofs, the figures, were ranged in columns before me,
When I was shown the charts and diagrams, to add, divide, and
    measure them,
When I sitting heard the astronomer where he lectured with
    much applause in the lecture-room,
How soon unaccountable I became tired and sick,
Till rising and gliding out I wander'd off by myself,
In the mystical moist night-air, and from time to time,
Look'd up in perfect silence at the stars.

WALT WHITMAN
1819 – 1892

Lightly Stepped a Yellow Star

Lightly stepped a yellow star
To its lofty place,
Loosed the Moon her silver hat
From her lustral face.
All of evening softly lit
As an astral hall –
'Father,' I observed to Heaven,
'You are punctual.'

EMILY DICKINSON
1830 – 1886

Reminiscence

The pale yellow receding sunset
Disappears in a wink of the eye.
Stilled are all motions,
Hushed all sounds.

A crow, already asleep,
Utters a throaty gurgle in the wind;
The silent, serene evening tide
Has overrun the whole city.

Street lamps aglow – a light blush,
An eagle glides down from the rampart,
Beneath the white blanket of mist at dusk
Rests the purple Chung mountain.

Through deserted alleys and lanes
Shaded by walls of palatial houses,
T'ang, sings the bamboo tube
Of an old dumpling peddler.

CHU HSIANG
1904 – 1933
Translated from the Chinese
by Kai-Yu Hsu

To Sleep

A flock of sheep that leisurely pass by,
One after one; the sound of rain, and bees
Murmuring; the fall of rivers, winds and seas,
Smooth fields, white sheets of water, and pure sky;
I have thought of all by turns, and yet do lie
Sleepless! and soon the small birds' melodies
Must hear, first uttered from my orchard trees;
And the first cuckoo's melancholy cry.
Even thus last night, and two nights more, I lay
And could not win thee, Sleep! by any stealth:
So do not let me wear to-night away:
Without Thee what is all the morning's wealth?
Come, blessèd barrier between day and day,
Dear mother of fresh thoughts and joyous health!

WILLIAM WORDSWORTH
1770 – 1850

Fragment

The mountain summits sleep, glens, cliffs, and caves
   Are silent; – all the black earth's reptile brood,
   The bees, the wild beasts of the mountain wood;
In depths beneath the dark red ocean's waves
   Its monsters rest; whilst, wrapt in bower and spray,
   Each bird is hush'd, that stretch'd its pinions to the day.

ALCMAN
7th Century, B.C.
Translated from the Greek
by Thomas Campbell

To the Night

Swiftly walk over the western wave,
        Spirit of Night!
Out of the misty eastern cave, –
Where, all the long and lone daylight,
Thou wovest dreams of joy and fear
Which make thee terrible and dear, –
        Swift be thy flight!

Wrap thy form in a mantle grey,
        Star-inwrought!
Blind with thine hair the eyes of Day;
Kiss her until she be wearied out.
Then wander o'er city and sea and land,
Touching all with thine opiate wand –
        Come, long-sought!

When I arose and saw the dawn
        I sigh'd for thee;
When light rode high, and the dew was gone,
And noon lay heavy on flower and tree,
And the weary Day turn'd to her rest,
Lingering like an unloved guest,
        I sigh'd for thee.

Thy brother Death came, and cried,
        'Wouldst thou me?'
Thy sweet child Sleep, the filmy-eyed,
Murmur'd like a noontide bee,
'Shall I nestle near thy side?
Wouldst thou me?' – And I replied,
        'No, not thee!'

Death will come when thou art dead,
Soon, too soon –
Sleep will come when thou art fled.
Of neither would I ask the boon
I ask of thee, belovèd Night –
Swift be thine approaching flight,
Come soon, soon!

PERCY BYSSHE SHELLEY
1792 – 1822

The Starlight Night

Look at the stars! look, look up at the skies!
  O look at all the fire-folk sitting in the air!
  The bright boroughs, the circle-citadels there!
Down in dim woods the diamond delves! the elves'-eyes!
The grey lawns cold where gold, where quickgold lies!
  Wind-beat whitebeam! airy abeles set on a flare!
  Flake-doves sent floating forth at a farmyard scare! –
Ah, well! it is all a purchase, all is a prize.

Buy then! bid then! – What? – Prayer, patience, alms, vows.
Look, look: a May-mess, like on orchard boughs!
  Look! March-bloom, like on mealed-with-yellow sallows!
These are indeed the barn; withindoors house
The shocks. This piece-bright paling shuts the spouse
  Christ home, Christ and his mother and all his hallows.

GERARD MANLEY HOPKINS
1844 – 1889

What Did I Lose?

I lost it – what did I lose
In this forest? At midnight I bring a lantern
To stroll in the woods to search;
I recognize the route paved with wild flowers,

Every tree, and every blade of grass. Ah, how did I
Lose it in a place so familiar!
What I lost must be right here, for
Next to this I know no other world.

With a lantern in hand I trace my way step by step.
The dewdrops, glistening, are weeping on the bough.
The stars wink above the trees,
All so quiet, so very quiet, all around.

Really, I did lose it in this place,
With a lantern I have been searching here every night,
But I could not find what I have lost,
Only I know that time hastens me along the path of age.

SUN YÜ-T'ANG
born 1905
Translated from the Chinese
by Kai-Yu Hsu

Meeting at Night

The grey sea and the long black land;
And the yellow half-moon large and low;
And the startled little waves that leap
In fiery ringlets from their sleep,
As I gain the cove with pushing prow,
And quench its speed i' the slushy sand.

Then a mile of warm sea-scented beach;
Three fields to cross till a farm appears;
A tap at the pane, the quick sharp scratch
And blue spurt of a lighted match,
And a voice less loud, thro' its joys and fears,
Than the two hearts beating each to each!

ROBERT BROWNING
1812 – 1869

Disillusionment of Ten O'Clock

The houses are haunted
By white night-gowns.
None are green,
Or purple with green rings,
Or green with yellow rings,
Or yellow with blue rings.
None of them are strange,
With socks of lace
And beaded ceintures.
People are not going
To dream of baboons and periwinkles.
Only, here and there, an old sailor,
Drunk and asleep in his boots,
Catches tigers
In red weather.

WALLACE STEVENS
1879 – 1955

From **L'Allegro**

To hear the Lark begin his flight,
And singing startle the dull night,
From his watch-towre in the skies,
Till the dappled dawn doth rise;
Then to com in spight of sorrow,
And at my window bid good morrow,
Through the Sweet-Briar, or the Vine,
Or the twisted Eglantine.
While the Cock with lively din,
Scatters the rear of darknes thin,
And to the stack, or the Barn dore,
Stoutly struts his Dames before,
Oft list'ning how the Hounds and horn
Chearly rouse the slumbring morn,
From the side of som Hoar Hill,
Through the high wood echoing shrill.
Som time walking not unseen
By Hedge-row Elms, on Hillocks green,
Right against the Eastern gate,
Wher the great Sun begins his state,
Rob'd in flames, and Amber light,
The clouds in thousand Liveries dight.
While the Plowman neer at hand,
Whistles ore the Furrow'd Land,
And the Milkmaid singeth blithe,
And the Mower whets his sithe,
And every Shepherd tells his tale
Under the Hawthorn in the dale.

JOHN MILTON
1608 – 1674

A Description of the Morning

Now hardly here and there an Hackney-Coach
Appearing, show'd the Ruddy Morn's Approach.
Now Betty from her Master's Bed had flown,
And softly stole to discompose her own.
The Slipshod 'Prentice from his Master's Dore,
Had par'd the Street, and Sprinkled round the Floor.
Now Moll had whirl'd her Mop with dext'rous Airs,
Prepar'd to scrub the Entry and the Stairs.
The Youth with broomy Stumps began to trace
The Kennel Edge, where Wheels had worn the Place.
The Smallcoal-Man was heard with Cadence deep,
Till drown'd in shriller Notes of Chimney-sweep.
Duns at his Lordship's Gate began to meet;
And Brickdust Moll had scream'd through half a street.
The Turn-key now his Flock returning sees,
Duly let out a'Nights to steal for Fees.
The watchfull Bayliffs take their silent Stands;
And School-boys lag with Satchels in their Hands.

JONATHAN SWIFT
1667 – 1743

Psalm of Those who Go Forth
before Daylight

The policeman buys shoes slow and careful; the teamster buys gloves slow and careful; they take care of their feet and hands; they live on their feet and hands.

The milkman never argues; he works alone and no one speaks to him; the city is asleep when he is on the job; he puts a bottle on six hundred porches and calls it a day's work; he climbs two hundred wooden stairways; two horses are company for him; he never argues.

The rolling-mill men and the sheet-steel men are brothers of cinders; they empty cinders out of their shoes after the day's work; they ask their wives to fix burnt holes in the knees of their trousers; their necks and ears are covered with a smut; they scour their necks and ears; they are brothers of cinders.

CARL SANDBURG
1878 – 1967

Notes

Some of the contributors and their works

All the poets are in alphabetical order. In the case of the Chinese poets the surname precedes the given name, according to the Chinese custom. For Japanese poets the Western order of names has been followed, with the exception of the seventeenth-century poet universally known as Matsuo Bashō.
For an explanation of *haiku, tanka* and *senryu,* see note under Shigeji Tsuboi.

ALCMAN C. 680 B.C. *Fragment*
A classical Greek poet who came as a slave to Sparta. He is sometimes called 'Alcman of Sparta'. Alcman was the founder of Doric lyric poetry and considered to be the inventor of the love song.

YAMAMURA BOCHŌ 1884 – 1924 *Cat*
A poet who was also a Christian minister and, at one time, a Buddhist priest. He was also associated with Hagiwara (usually regarded as Japan's first 'modern' poet). He edited various poetry magazines and lived in almost continual sickness and poverty. His haunting work shows strong Surrealist influences, later becoming humanist and serene.

CHU HSIANG 1904 – 33 *A Rainy Scene*
A modern Chinese poet, born in Anhwei Province. As a boy, he studied classical Chinese literature and also English, and developed a passion for Scott, Stevenson and Shakespeare. For a while he was a student at the University of Chicago. His short lyrics, with their clear, crisp imagery, are especially successful. He experimented with language and rhythm, and even translated Shelley's poems into Chinese, using their original metres. Like so many poets, he was not a happy man, and drowned himself in the Huang-p'u River near Shanghai on 4 December 1933.

E. E. CUMMINGS 1894 – 1962 *spring is like a perhaps hand*
Here is a modern American poet whose printed 'shapes' in

L   161 poetry are most original and amusing, and often startling. Look at the exciting way he uses that dull thing, punctuation! We might say that he is the 'Poet of Punctuation'. Punctuation is very important in a poem, more so than in prose, for punctuation is a kind of musical notation used deliberately by the poet to guide us in our reading, either silent or aloud, of his work. Without good punctuation we cannot group the words easily or follow the rhythms. In Cummings, punctuation is a pleasure, and an integral part of the imagery, ideas and shape of his work. As you might expect from the look of his poems on the page, he composed directly on to his typewriter.

SAKUTARO HAGIWARA 1886 – 1942 *An Octopus which Did Not Die*
The 'father' of modern Japanese poetry, he used colloquial language and non-classical, Western forms. This poem is written in prose form, but it is a poem all the same. There are many prose passages in English literature – for example, in the Bible and in novels and essays – which in their beauty of sound and poetic use of words and images are unmistakably poems.

GERARD MANLEY HOPKINS 1844 – 89 *Inversnaid*
Most of the poems in this book should be read aloud, either on one's own or in choral speaking. This poem sounds splendid when read aloud in chorus.

THE PRIEST JAKUREN died 1202 *Autumn Loneliness*
This early Japanese poem is in the classical *tanka* or *waka* form, and was published in a collection of poems called the *Shinkokinshu* in 1205. It is both elegant and poignant; the original is indeed highly sophisticated, and its technical perfection is lost in translation. It is surprisingly modern in tone.

YUJI KINOSHITA born 1914 *A Winter Fountain*
This very refined Japanese lyricist is also both traditional and modern. Like the work of most modern Japanese poets, his poetry shows the influence of French Surrealist poets.

JAMES KIRKUP born 1923 *Thunder and Lightning*
This poem describes, in Japanese *haiku* style, adapted to a modern English form, a thunderstorm over the village of Corsham in Wiltshire, where the author lived for three years. He was once struck by lightning in a tram-car so this perhaps explains his fear of thunderstorms.

162

JOHN LENNON born 1940   *The National Health Cow*
The John Lennon lyrics will be familiar to everyone for the remarkable and often beautiful songs he has written with Paul McCartney. John Lennon is one of the most gifted of younger English poets, and certainly one of the best writers of comic and fantastic verse ever produced by England.

LI KUANG-T'IEN born 1907   *The Scent of Autumn*
This poet, born in a small village in Shantung Province, reflects in his work the simple farming life, and the plants, birds and insects of his childhood. This poem was written in September 1931, and appeared in a volume called *The Han Garden*. He admires the English nature writers Gilbert White and W. H. Hudson. Since 1936 he has written no poetry.

LIU TA-PAI 1880 – 1932   *The Spirit of Spring*
One of the leaders of the 'new literature' movement in China in the early years of this century. Though an expert in Chinese classical style, Liu Ta-Pai advocated the use of ordinary colloquial speech in poetry. Even in his vernacular poems, we can still feel his classical scholarship and firm technique grounded on traditional forms. He often writes of nature, solitude and the four seasons, just as do English poets, and Japanese poets, who were much influenced in the past by Chinese forms. This poem about spring was written, we are told, 'in a boat at Hsiao-shan, 29 March 1923'.

MAO TSE-TUNG born 1893   *Winter Clouds*
A poet with a deep admiration for classical forms and the classical poets of China, such as Lu Yu and Yueh Fei of the Sung Dynasty. This poem was composed by Chairman Mao on 26 December 1962, his sixty-ninth birthday. Chairman Mao in this poem refers indirectly, in typical Chinese allusive fashion, to the 'cold war' between Russia and China. 'The brave have no fear of bears' is his own way of saying he is not afraid of Russia, and that the Chinese people are brave enough to endure the extreme cold of Sino-Soviet relations. Chairman Mao is the only great statesman in our times who is also a considerable poet.

KAORU MARUYAMA born 1899   *The Estuary*
Maruyama founded a famous Japanese modern poetry magazine called *Shiki* and was the intimate friend of another famous modern Japanese poet represented in this anthology, Sakutaro Hagiwara. Maruyama is particularly well known as a poet of

163

the sea. Like many of the works by modern poets, this poem reminds us of an Impressionist picture, for Japanese, Chinese and most Oriental poets are generally concerned with visual images and sounds rather than with ideas or arguments.

MATSUO BASHŌ 1644–94   *At Kisagata*
This is an example of a traditional *haiku* by Japan's most famous *haiku* poet. He made many journeys on foot on the main island of Honshu, and as he wandered from place to place he kept diaries in which vivid prose descriptions were mixed with these brief, melodious *haiku*. He was a contemporary of English poets such as Cowley, Crashaw, Dryden and Herrick (whose poems about the fleetingness of life and the death of flowers have a definite *haiku* spirit). You may find other English poems in this book which seem to show the qualities of *haiku*.

KAZUMASA NAKAGAWA born 1892   *Anemone*
As might be expected from what the poet writes in this poem, he is also a painter, celebrated both for his classical Japanese *sumie*, or Indian ink paintings, and for his modern Western-style compositions in oils. In Japanese and Chinese poetry, verse and painting have always been intimately connected, and very often we can see scrolls in which poems are part of the painting. Compare the English poet William Blake who combined art and poetry in a similar way.

HARUO SATŌ born 1892   *Song of the Mackerel Pike*
A novelist as well as a poet.

SHAN MEI   *The Green Spring*
A fine young Chinese poet whose first book, *I'm a Newcomer*, in which this poem appears, was published in Shanghai in 1941.

SUN YÜ-T'ANG born 1905   *What Did I Lose?*
This poet belonged to a new Chinese group of poets calling themselves 'The Crescent School'. They tried to express new ideas and new images in poetry, using new verse forms and popular language. This is an extract from a long poem, *The Precious Horse* (1939).

D. H. THOMAS born 1948   *Washing Day*
This schoolboy, a pupil of the poet Robert Morgan, wrote this very vivid poem about the sights and smells of washing day when he was fifteen.

SHIGEJI TSUBOI born 1889 *A Stone*
A leading modern Japanese poet, he founded the New Japan
Literature Society. Like the work of many modern Japanese poets,
his poems are modern in style, but owe a great deal to the
traditional forms of Japanese verse such as *haiku* (three-line
poems composed of 5, 7 and 5 syllables); *tanka* (five-line poems
composed of 5, 7, 5, 7 and 7 syllables); and *senryu* which are like
haiku but more biting and satirical in tone. *Haiku* and *tanka* try
to capture the essence of things, seasons and feelings in a few
sharp and sometimes startlingly contrasted images. The Japanese
have very strict rules for writing these traditional forms of poetry,
but the rules are often broken, especially when these poems are
written by children, who often write extremely vivid *haiku* or
haiku-like poems. In this book you will find many *haiku* in
traditional form and also in the 'free' form used by children and
modern poets. Among the English poets, look carefully at Thom
Gunn's *Considering the Snail*, and you will see that this is a
perfectly syllabic poem.

SHIZUE UEDA born 1898 *Gold Fan*
A very sensitive Japanese woman poet whose work is remarkable
for the delicacy of its colour, imagery and sound. A gingko tree
has fan-shaped leaves which resemble, in many ways, the maiden-
hair fern.

ARTHUR WALEY 1889 – 1966 *The Little Cart*
Arthur Waley is famous as the inspired translator of much
classical Chinese and Japanese literature. One of his most
delightful translations is of the anonymous, twelfth-century
Japanese tale called *The Lady who Loved Insects*. Children will
enjoy this, as well as parts of his splendid version of Lady
Murasaki's *The Tale of Genji*.

PHILIP WONNACOTT born 1957 *The Fox*
This schoolboy, a pupil of the poet Charles Causley, wrote his
poem at the age of seven. It is a piece of fine, direct, clear-eyed
observation, yet shows true poetic imagination and a certain free
fantasy in its language.

BAKU YAMANOGUCHI 1903 – 63 *A Rat*
He was born in Okinawa, and after graduation came to Tokyo
where he led a vagabond existence. His complete poems were
published in 1958. He was one of the rare Japanese 'outsiders'
in both society and literature. He died in poverty in 1963.

Index of first lines

'Grass afield wears silver thatch, 43

Happy the man, whose wish and care, 17
Hard by the lilied Nile I saw, 124
Having cast away, 91
He clasps the crag with crooked hands, 106
Here at the wayside station, as many a morning, 21
Here lies, whom hound did ne'er pursue, 86
Here's a song, 53
He rises and begins to round, 108
How large unto the tiny fly, 138
Hugging the ground by the lilac tree, 85

I am his Highness' dog at Kew, 95
I caught a tremendous fish, 120
I climbed through woods in the hour-before-dawn dark, 92
I dreamed that, as I wandered by the way, 58
I found a ball of grass among the hay, 84
I got me flowers to straw Thy way, 57
I hear a sudden cry of pain, 83
I imagine this midnight moment's forest, 89
I know some lonely houses off the road, 142
I like to toss him up and down, 97
I lost it – what did I lose, 156
In moving-slow he has no Peer, 81
In sea-cold Lyonesse, 35
In the northern hemisphere, 100
In your pupils, 99
I strolled into a farmyard, 98
I think I could turn and live with animals, 102
I woke in the swimming dark, 44

Lightless, unholy, eldritch thing, 96
Lightly stepped a yellow star, 151
Like trains of cars on tracks of plush, 135
Little Fly, 134
Little Lamb, who made thee, 88
Loneliness does not, 66
Look at the stars! look, look up at the skies, 155
Look, stranger, on this island now, 18
Low-anchored cloud, 65

Index of authors

Thomas, D. H., 143
Thomas, Edward, 115
Thoreau, Henry David, 65
Tokunaga, Shozo (*translator*), 65, 91, 127
Tsuboi, Shigeji, 17
Tsuno, Hideyuki, 48

Ueda, Shizue, 65

Waley, Arthur (*translator*), 144
Whitman, Walt, 36, 102, 113, 151
Williams, Alfred, 114
Williams, William Carlos, 75
Wilson, Graeme (*translator*), 84
Wither, George, 26
Wonnacott, Philip, 82
Wordsworth, William, 153

Yamada, Tokiyo, 19
Yamanoguchi, Baku, 91
Yeats, William Butler, 109
Young, Andrew, 116

Acknowledgements

Grateful acknowledgements are made to the following for permission to reprint copyright material:

GEORGE ALLEN & UNWIN LTD for 'At Kisagata' and 'Autumn Loneliness' from *An Anthology of Japanese Literature* edited by Donald Keene, and 'The Little Cart' from *Chinese Poems* by Arthur Waley

JONATHAN CAPE LTD for 'The National Health Cow' from *A Spaniard in the Works* by John Lennon

BRUNO CASSIRER LTD for the quotation used opposite the copyright page from *Report to Greco* by Nikos Kazantzakis

CHAPMAN & HALL LTD for 'My Cats' from *Harold's Leap* by Stevie Smith

CHATTO & WINDUS LTD for 'Summer Farm' from *A Common Grace* by Norman MacCaig; CHATTO & WINDUS LTD and THE HOUGHTON MIFFLIN COMPANY for 'The Fish' from *Poems* by Elizabeth Bishop

THE CRESSET PRESS for 'The Country Bedroom' from *The Collected Poems of Frances Cornford*, and 'The Bat' from *Urania* by Ruth Pitter

THE LITERARY TRUSTEES OF WALTER DE LA MARE and THE SOCIETY OF AUTHORS as their representatives for 'Sunk Lyonesse', 'Rain', 'Snow' and 'The Fly' from *The Collected Poems of Walter de la Mare*

J. M. DENT & SONS LTD for 'Man and Beast' from *Poems 1935-1948* by Clifford Dyment

ANDRÉ DEUTSCH LTD for 'Apples' from *My Many-Coated Man* by Laurie Lee

DOUBLEDAY & CO. INC. for 'The Spirit of Spring', 'A Rainy Scene', 'The Green Spring', 'White Butterfly', 'The Scent of Autumn', 'What Did I Lose?' and 'Reminiscence' from *Twentieth Century Chinese Poetry* edited by Kai-Yu Hsu, and 'The Sloth' from *The Collected Poems of Theodore Roethke*

FABER & FABER LTD for 'On This Island' from *Collected Shorter Poems* by W. H. Auden, 'Considering the Snail' from *My Sad Captains* by Thom Gunn, and 'The Wayside Station' from *Collected Poems* by Edwin Muir; FABER & FABER LTD and HARCOURT, BRACE & WORLD INC. for 'spring is like a perhaps hand' from *Poems 1923-1954* by e. e. cummings, Copyright 1925 by E. E. Cummings; FABER & FABER LTD and HARPER & ROW INC. for 'The Horses' and 'The Thought-Fox' from *Hawk in the Rain* by Ted Hughes, Copyright 1957 by Ted Hughes; FABER & FABER LTD and RANDOM HOUSE INC., ALFRED A. KNOPF INC. AND DIVISIONS for 'Disillusionment of Ten O'Clock' from *The Collected Poems of Wallace Stevens*